CONSTRUCTION EQUIPMENT

James E. Russell

Reston Publishing Company, Inc.
A Prentice-Hall Company
Reston, Virginia

Library of Congress Cataloging in Publication Data

Russell, James E. (James Emerson)
  Construction equipment.

  Includes index.
  1. Construction equipment.   I. Title.
TH900.R69   1985   624.1'028   84-27713
ISBN 0-8359-0954-9

10   9   8   7   6   5   4   3   2   1

PRINTED IN THE UNITED STATES OF AMERICA

CONTENTS

PREFACE

The goal of any book on construction equipment use and management must be to help the reader learn to match equipment to the type, size, and physical conditions of each particular project to be done—within the operating needs of the company.

To a newcomer to the study of construction equipment, this may be a bewildering goal. For example, an inexperienced person watching a big construction project from the sidewalk is apt to be overwhelmed by the complexity of the activities. Bustling earthmovers, huge off-highway trucks, crawler tractors, cranes, and other equipment all appear to be operating independently of each other.

In fact, however, each piece of machinery is an integral part of the whole fleet, contributing harmoniously to the goals of the project just as certainly as each instrument in a symphony orchestra contributes to the total effect heard by the audience.

It appears to me, then, that one of the more important tasks of an equipment text like this one is to help the reader develop a creative overview of equipment use, a *feel* for the selection of the machinery that will make the job flow. After this feel is achieved, the technical aspects of equipment selection and management may be approached with more confidence. Thus, I have structured the book from a generalized beginning to a more technical end.

I hope this arrangement proves helpful to my readers.

ACKNOWLEDGMENTS

I am much indebted to the following manufacturers and associations for the photos and artwork, charts, graphs, and other aids seen in this text and for help and advice with the text itself.

American Hoist & Derrick
American Plywood Association
Barber-Greene
Bil-Jax, Inc.
Butler Trailer
Case
Caterpillar Tractor
Construction Industry Manufacturers Association
CECO
Clark Michigan
John Deere
Eagle Iron Works
FMC
Ford
Gill
Hudson Brothers Trailer
Hyster
Ingersoll-Rand
International-Hough
Insley
Kinshofer
Koehring
Patent Scaffolding
Portec/Kolberg
Power Crane and Shovel Association
Rome Industries
RO Corporation
Symons
Talbert Trailer
Universal Forms
Vermeer
Wabco

1

BASIC CONSIDERATIONS

Any construction project may be broken down into the three basic management-related areas of planning, scheduling, and supervision. A knowledge of the characteristics, capabilities, and application of construction equipment is essential to each of these.

Planning the use of construction equipment involves selecting the best equipment for the particular task(s) to be accomplished. Proper use of equipment contributes to project efficiency, thus reducing time-related costs and maintenance costs. And, of course, reducing these operational costs increases profit. Two of the most useful tools for construction equipment and project planning are an individual's past job experience and records and the manufacturer's data.

Scheduling the use of construction equipment involves studying past production records and modifying the statistics obtained from those records in accordance with such factors as weather, field conditions, operator experience, the condition of existing and proposed equipment, and other items that influence the job at hand.

Supervision requirements can be determined after the job is analyzed and the equipment needs and schedule are ascertained. Jobs and supervision requirements vary considerably, from several workers with simple equipment and a single supervisor to mammoth projects requiring dozens of pieces of equipment and many specialists and supervisors.

The maintenance of good production records helps construction managers estimate production and arrive at schedules. Management decisions may then be made and production control can be more certain. It is almost always necessary to alter the original project plans as the project progresses. But these alterations should not be extreme, and the job should be completed on or before the scheduled completion date.

Thus, an organized method of reporting, directing, and recording production progress should be used. The following terms may be helpful, although individual managers and companies often have their own methods and terms.

Work done. Work done is just what the term implies. It may be 50 concrete foundations installed, 10,000 board-feet of timber cut, 5,000 cubic yards of gravel placed, 100 miles traveled, or any similar task completed as long as it can be expressed quantitatively and the appropriate units (of volume, weight, etc.) are used.

Units of time. Units of time pass as work done progresses. Such units may be an eight-hour day, 30 man-hours, a six-month project, etc. Obviously, they vary with the situation. You would not normally speak, for example, of a 480-minute work day.

Production. Production is always related to time—e.g., cubic yards of gravel per hour, tons per shift (shift time varies and thus must be noted), board-feet of lumber per day, etc. The *rate of production* is expressed by the simple formula

$$\text{Rate of production} = \frac{\text{Work done}}{\text{Unit of time}}$$

Another simple formula, frequently used in scheduling projects, is

$$\text{Time required} = \frac{\text{Time period}}{\text{Unit of work done}}$$

Quantities satisfying this formula are, for example, 8 hours per 10,000 cubic yards of gravel moved, 30 days per acre prepared, and .25 minute per foot of ditch. The particular work task and/or piece of equipment has its own most convenient units of time and work done. This text will employ commonly used units; but the important thing for the user is to keep the units straight both in the mind and on the records.

MATERIALS

The physical characteristics of a material largely determine how easy or difficult it is to move. The ease or difficulty of moving a material may be called its *loadability*. Loadability is a general term: materials that can be loaded easily without special equipment or attachments are said to have a high degree of loadability; materials that are difficult to load and require special equipment and/or special attachments have a low degree of loadability. For example, a sandy loam soil may be easily loaded from the natural state with a dozer. Clay is also easily loaded; scrapers often load both of these materials. On the other hand, rock, hardpan, and soils with heavy roots intact may require loosening before loading. Rippers are often used to loosen such soil, and in extreme cases blasting may be necessary.

To help determine loadability, materials may be divided into the three broad categories of rock, soil, and rock–soil mixtures.

Rock may of course be boulders, ledges, heavy stone, and the like. But for purposes of establishing degree of loadability, rock is also masonry, concrete, and similar hard materials frequently encountered in concrete work. All remaining materials are considered soil or rock–soil mixtures.

Soil is classified according to where it falls within a range of standard particle sizes and types. For instance, clay is composed of tiny, flaky particles.

At the other extreme, gravel is composed of relatively large rocky particles. Other materials, e.g., sand and silt, fall somewhere in between.

Rock–soil mixtures, as the term implies, are composed of both rock and soil.

In determining the overall loadability of a project, a careful study of the area must be made, in which the predominant materials and any unusual loading problem that may be present are noted. (For example, one might record that the terrain is predominantly a rock–soil mixture with some rock outcrops and ledges.)

MOISTURE

Moisture affects both the weight of a material and its handleability. Thus, moisture affects loadability. Most materials contain some moisture in their natural states, the amount of which depends on such factors as the weather, drainage, and the ability of the material to hold moisture.

Moisture within a material can sometimes be changed, in which case the loadability of the material will be changed. Marsh land, for example, has a higher degree of loadability if the land can first be drained and allowed to dry. Conversely, an ordinarily fairly dry soil may have a much lower degree of loadability in the rainy season than in the dry season.

WEIGHT, VOLUME, AND SWELL

The weight and volume of materials affect both the type of equipment selected and the performance of the equipment. For example, suppose a truck can carry 25 cubic yards of material that weighs a maximum of 50,000 pounds (25 tons). If the load is a light material, such as cinders, then the machine will be filled much sooner than its load capacity is reached. Thus, another machine and/or arrangement—e.g., a truck or tractor with one or more towed trailers— should be considered. Conversely, if the preceding truck is loaded with gravel that weighs 3,000 pounds (1.5 tons) per cubic yard, its maximum weight capacity will be exceeded before its maximum volume is reached. Thus, equipment should be selected with a view toward the weight and volume of material it will handle.

Swell is the additional volume created when a material is removed from its natural or "bank" condition. This extra volume is due to the numerous voids created in the material when it is moved. The swell of specific materials can be predicted and is expressed as a percentage increase in volume.

COMPACTIBILITY

Compactibility may be thought of as the ability of a material to be compressed more tightly than it would normally sit in bank condition. Soil must be well compacted for roads, foundations, and similar uses in which a very stable base is necessary. Thus, more soil is required where compaction will be done.

LOAD FACTOR

The load factor determines the volume of loose yard measure to bank yard measure. For example, the load factor for dry clay is 0.72. Thus, if a scraper is carrying a load of 25 cubic yards of dry clay to be used in bank condition at the building site, then the scraper is carrying 25×0.72, or only 18.0, bank cubic yards. Similar calculations are made for material to be compacted.

Clearly, the loadability, swell, weight, and compaction characteristics of materials must be analyzed when selecting construction equipment, planning its use, arriving at schedules, and computing costs. All these factors will be analyzed more thoroughly in the chapter on production estimating.

ZONES OF OPERATION

Zones of operation may be helpful on large projects. These zones are the power zone, the slow-speed hauling zone, and the high-speed hauling zone. (See Figure 1–1.)

The *power zone* requires tractors with high drawbar pulls at slow speeds to overcome adverse site conditions. It makes extensive use of the crawler tractor with a dozer blade.

The *slow-speed hauling zone* has slightly improved site conditions over the power zone. The crawler tractor is still the basic machine, but better conditions allow power to tow earth-hauling scrapers. Rubber-tired vehicles do not reach their potential in this zone because they are not able to shift to high gears.

In the *high-speed hauling zone,* ground conditions or roads permit long hauls at high speed. Thus, the rubber-tired tractor and scraper combination is used.

To increase production, it is necessary to get the site into the high-speed hauling zone condition as rapidly as possible. Of course, this may not happen

Zones of operation.

Figure 1–1. On large projects, time may be saved by planning the routes of various machinery so that optimum speeds may be maintained. Source: U.S. Army

over the whole site simultaneously. Rather, haul roads may be established and put into operation on some parts of the site while other parts remain in the first two zones.

VALUE ENGINEERING

Traditionally, architects and/or engineers have designed projects for owners and may continue to represent the owners in obtaining contractors and, later, in seeing that the work is completed according to the terms of the contract(s) and according to plans and specifications. Under this relationship, it is the architect or engineer's responsibility to see that the project has been designed to serve the owner's needs and desires at a reasonable cost.

The same basic relationship exists today. However, a specialized discipline has recently evolved which sometimes modifies the traditional contractual relationship. This special discipline is called *value engineering*. Simply put, *value engineering attempts to cut project costs*. The value engineering firm may be engaged during the production of plans and specifications or at their completion, before they are let out for bids. The value engineer attempts to find ways to modify the design or materials of a structure in order to effect savings without sacrificing design or construction quality. All savings found at this point in the project history (minus the cost of the study) usually go to the owner.

If a value engineer is not used before bids are requested, the contractor, after reviewing the plans and specifications, may contract with a value engineer to review them. Or the contractor may employ a full-time value engineer within the contracting firm. Under this arrangement, any savings found are usually shared by the owner and the contractor. Regardless of when the value engineer is brought into the picture, the owner must agree to any changes made in the plans, specifications, and other contract documents. Moreover, the changes should be reviewed with the architect and/or engineer before approval is given.

A full treatment of value engineering is beyond the scope of this text. Readers who desire to pursue value engineering in depth will find good texts on the subject in most libraries. However, the following examples will be helpful in understanding the basic function of value engineering.

Example   In analyzing plans and specifications for a garden apartment complex, a value engineer determines that trusses may be substituted for on-site framing. The trusses prove to be initially cheaper and reduce the amount of labor required for framing the apartments. Furthermore, the trusses may be installed more quickly and thus allow the contractor to get the project under roof before the rainy season begins, thereby making it possible to begin interior work earlier. Significant savings may be realized without sacrificing either design or quality of materials.

Example   In a single-story development, it is discovered that a monolithic floor slab and foundation may be used instead of the separate footing, foundation wall, and floor slab shown on the plans. By pouring the floor slab and foundation in one operation, significant savings may be realized.

These examples are deliberately simple, for the purpose of illustration. Any architect or engineer should be alert to such generally known construction efficiencies. However, on large projects, such as dams, high-rise buildings, large-scale housing developments, shopping centers, bridges, and tunnels, modifications that produce savings may not be so obvious. Thus, the scale and complexity of the project is a factor in deciding whether or not a value engineer is needed. Regardless of the complexity of the project, however, the value engineer must answer certain basic questions about the project to determine whether modifications that lead to savings can be made. The following questions are typical:

1. What are the functions of the project?
2. How do the materials relate to the function and design of the project?
3. Are there any alternative materials that could be used that would be cheaper to buy and easier to install?

4. What construction methods are anticipated, and are there alternative methods that might be used that would speed up construction or reduce the amount of labor needed?

As mentioned earlier, the architect or engineer is normally the owner's representative. However, an architect who specializes in a particular building type, say, hospitals, may be offended at an owner's suggestion that a value engineer look over the plans and specifications. The architect may believe that he or she should have the authority to decide whether such a professional is needed, and if so, to seek out the required individual. A structural engineer in the same specialty might be similarly offended. Thus, since contractors often depend on architects and engineers for other kinds of recommendations, they may be hesitant to suggest contacting a value engineer, fearing that it would challenge the architect or engineer's professional ability and integrity.

Exercising professional tact should avoid any problems regarding the use of value engineers. On any project, cooperation between the various professions is a vital factor that affects both the cost and quality of the project. Therefore, it is essential that each of the professionals involved—architects, engineers, developers, owners, and value engineers—understand the professional and contractual responsibilities of the others. They must work together in a spirit of mutual respect and cooperation.

2

THE CRITICAL-PATH METHOD OF CONSTRUCTION SCHEDULING

The critical-path method (CPM) of construction scheduling is a graphic tool that enables construction managers to see the elements of the project that are most critical to meeting the schedule. Using this method, the manager can plan a project and analyze any or all of the tasks within it during and after construction.

CPM scheduling begins with a simple listing of the tasks to be performed. Detail is important in the listing. For instance, the act of installing foundation footings could include all of the following tasks, depending on the complexity of the footings:

1. Stake footing trench location.

2. Dig footing trenches.

3. Install formwork.

4. Install reinforcing.

5. Pour concrete footing.

6. Screed footing level.

7. Pour foundation wall.

There might in fact be considerably more detail than that shown. And the task definitely would not be adequately described for CPM purposes as simply "install foundation footings."

In using CPM, three questions must be answered about each task as it relates to the other tasks within the project:

1. Which tasks must be finished before this one can be started?

2. Which tasks cannot be started until this one is finished?

3. Which tasks may start or finish as this one starts or finishes?

Another way of asking the same questions is:

1. Which tasks have precedence?

2. Which tasks must be accomplished in succession?

3. Which tasks may be accomplished concurrently?

Activities. In CPM, the building tasks are called *activities.* These activities can be, and often are, off the job site and not physically connected to the job. (Consider, for example, the activities "obtain building permit" and "acquire cement.")

Network. When the foregoing three questions are answered, it is possible to graphically arrange the activities connected with a project in an ordered sequence or pattern called a *network.* In the network, each activity is represented

Figure 2–1. This activity may be referred to as "acquire building permit" or "activity 2–5"; or, where it is more convenient, the activity may be represented by a letter.

by an arrow, the tail of which represents the start of the activity and the head of which represents the completion of the activity. Thus, the arrow points toward completion of the activity. Each arrow is labeled with the activity it represents, and its length is arbitrary. That is, the length of the arrow has nothing to do with how long it takes to complete the activity.

Events. An *event* is the completion of an activity. Events are represented by circles, usually with a number inside. An event may be given any convenient number, but event numbers at the head of an arrow must be larger than those at the tail. After events are numbered, specific activities may be referred to either by name or by the pair of event numbers that enclose the activity. For convenience, activities are often assigned code letters, so that, for example, "acquire building permit" might become simply *A*. (See Figure 2–1.)

Network Logic. One of the advantages of the graphic network is that, through the use of *network logic,* it helps managers avoid mistakes in scheduling. The key idea is that *activities leaving an event cannot begin until all of the activities heading into that event have been completed.* (See Figure 2–2.) Notice that

1. Activity *A* must be finished before activity *B* can begin.
2. Activities *C* and *D* must be finished before activity *G* can begin.
3. Activity *I* must be completed before activities *D* and *H* can begin.
4. Activities *C* and *D* may end at the same time.
5. Activities *D* and *H* may start at the same time.

In this manner, errors in scheduling are more difficult to make.

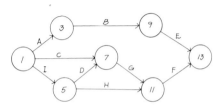

Figure 2–2. Network logic of activities.

Dummy Activities. Dummy activities are often needed to maintain network logic. These activities take zero time and show only relationships of sequence. Dummy activities are represented by dashed arrows.

Example

Let us say we wish to lay a concrete slab and build a gravel road nearby. Water for the concrete and other uses is readily available at all times. It is possible, and cost effective, to use the same gravel for our concrete mix that we are using for the road. In thinking about the project, we find that

1. Building the road depends on having the gravel.
2. Making the concrete mix depends on having both the gravel and the cement.
3. Building the road does not depend on having the cement.

Figure 2–3 shows the completed network for the concrete slab and gravel road. The *dummy activity,* represented by the dashed arrow,

1. Has no name.
2. Takes zero time.
3. Is used to show that the building of the road may proceed without having cement but that the concrete cannot be mixed without having gravel.

Another use for dummy activities is to eliminate duplication of event numbers. Each activity must have a unique identification, e.g., activity *A,* activity *B,* etc. These same activities may also be identified by their event numbers.

In Figure 2–4(a), activities *A* and *B* both begin at event 5 and end at event 8. Thus, both may be identified as activity 5–8. To prevent this duplication, a dummy activity arrow may be used, as in Figure 2–4(b).

Remember that (1) dummy activity arrows show only relationships of sequence, and (2) the length of an activity arrow has nothing to do with the time required to complete the activity.

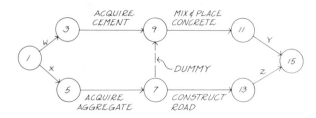

Figure 2–3. Dummy activity.

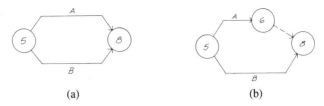

Figure 2–4. (a) Event duplication. (b) Dummy arrow used to prevent event duplication.

Duration. Duration is the estimated amount of time required to complete an activity. Any appropriate time unit may be used. Durations are figured using conventional production estimating methods, with times placed above the appropriate activity arrows.

Event Times. Event times should be figured next. In CPM, an event occurs or is reached the moment that all the activities that go to the event circle are completed. Thus, while event circles themselves have no time aspect, they represent the end of one or more time periods (minutes, hours, days, months, years, etc.). Also, activities that follow a given event cannot begin until the activity or activities that go to the event are completed and the event has occurred.

Earliest Event Times and Latest Event Times. To calculate event times, we must estimate the earliest and latest times the events can occur. Earliest event times are abbreviated EETs, and latest event times LETs. The network shown in Figure 2–5 illustrates how EETs are applied.

Observe that the EETs are placed in small *squares* above or next to the event circles. Since event 1 has no activities going into it, no activities have been completed before the occurrence of event 1, and a zero is placed in the square over it. The EET for event 3 is $0+4=4$. Adding this to duration 3–9, which is 3, we get $4+3=7$. Thus, since whenever there is a choice of EETs the larger one is always used, the duration of event 9 is 7 (not 3, the duration of activity 1–9). All EETs for events are calculated in this manner.

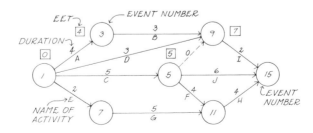

Figure 2–5. Network with earliest event times (EETs) added.

The EET for the entire project is the path from the first event to the last event that results in the largest EET. For example, moving from events 1 to 3 to 9 to 15 gives a project EET of 9. Similarly, moving from events 1 to 5 to 11 to 15 gives a project EET of 13. Thus, the EET for the entire project is 13.

After the EETs have been computed, the LETs may be calculated. LETs are placed in *triangles* underneath the event circles. (See Figure 2–6.)

The first assumption in calculating LETs is that the LET for the ending event is the same as the EET for the ending event. We then calculate the LETs by working backwards from the end event along the activity arrows, subtracting as we go. When there is a choice of LETs, we select the *smallest* one (the opposite from calculating EETs).

In Figure 2–6, working backwards from event 15, we want to find the LET for event 11. The duration of event 15 is 13; the duration of activity 11–15 is 4. Thus, the LET for event 11 is $13 - 4 = 9$.

There are three choices for paths emanating backwards from event 5: the path from event 5 to 9 to 15; from 5 to 15; and from 5 to 11 to 15. Working with the 5 to 9 to 15 path, we get $13 - 2 - 0$ (the dummy) $= 11$. With the 5 to 15 path, we get $13 - 6 = 7$. And with the 5 to 11 to 15 path, we get $13 - 4 - 4 = 5$, which is the smallest LET. Thus, the LET for event 5 is 5 and is represented with a triangle underneath. All LETs for events are calculated in this manner.

After the EETs and LETs are calculated, critical activities may be found. A *critical activity* is an activity which, if delayed, will delay the entire project the same length of time as the critical activity is delayed. Critical activities are those which conform to the following conditions:

1. The earliest and latest event times at the tail of the activity arrow are equal.

2. The earliest and latest event times at the head of the activity arrow are equal.

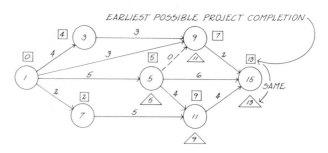

Figure 2–6. Network with latest event times (LETs) added.

3. The EET (LET) at the head of the activity arrow minus the EET (LET) at the tail of the activity arrow is equal to the duration of the activity.

All three of the above conditions must be met before the activity is considered critical.

Critical Path. The critical path of a network is a kind of summation of the critical activities. When complete, a critical path of activities will stretch from the beginning event to the end event of the network. The following rules will help identify the critical path of a network (see Figure 2–7):

1. The critical path is a continuous, unbroken path from the beginning event to the end event. If the path is broken, or begins or ends in the middle of the network, a mistake has been made.

2. There is always at least one, and perhaps more than one, critical path in any network.

3. The sum of the durations along the critical path in the direction of the activity arrows is always the length of time required to complete the entire project.

In Figure 2–7, activity 5–11 is critical, because:

1. The earliest and latest event times at the tail of the activity arrow are equal.

2. The earliest and latest event times at the head of the activity arrow are equal.

3. The EET at the head of the arrow minus the EET at the tail of the arrow equals the duration of activity 5–11; and the LET at the head of the arrow minus the LET at the tail of the arrow equals the duration of activity 5–11.

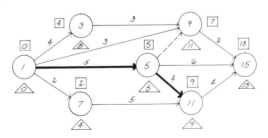

Figure 2–7. Network with critical path displayed.

Similarly, activity 1-5 is critical and completes the critical path of the network. It should be noted that even dummy activities may be critical, as long as they satisfy the preceding conditions. The critical path of a network should be made darker, wider, or a different color, or should otherwise be distinguished from the other paths of the network so that it visibly stands out from them.

Tabulation of Activity Times. Before a construction schedule can be made, it is necessary to tabulate the activity times. Activity times may be calculated by the following formulas:

1. $ES = \Box$ or EET at the tail of the activity arrow.

2. $EF = ES + DUR$

3. $LS = LF - DUR$

4. $LF = \Delta$ or LET at the head of the activity arrow.

5. $TF = LS - ES = LF - EF$

where

ES = the earliest time the activity can start.

EF = the earliest time the activity can finish.

DUR = the duration of the activity.

LS = the latest time the activity can start and not delay the project.

LF = the latest time the activity can be finished and not delay the project.

TF = *total float,* or scheduling leeway. Activities with no total float are on the critical path.

DUR is copied from the network. Also, since for a given activity ES is simply the EET at the tail of the activity arrow and LF is the LET at the head of the arrow, ES and LF are copied from the network.

Example   Let us tabulate $DUR, ES, EF, LS, LF,$ and TF for activity 1–3 of Figure 2–7. $DUR,$ taken directly from the network, is 4. Since the EET at the tail of the activity is zero, $ES = 0$. $EF = ES + DUR = 0 + 4 = 4$. LF (Δ or LET at the head of the activity arrow), copied directly from the network, is 8. $LS = LF - DUR, = 8 - 4 = 4$. Finally, $TF = LS - ES = 4 - 0 = 4$; or, alternatively,

Table 2–1. Tabulation Sheet.

ACTIVITY	DURATION	EARLY START	EARLY FINISH	LATE START	LATE FINISH	TOTAL FLOAT
1–3	4	0	4	4	8	4
1–5	5	0	5	0	5	0
1–7	2	0	2	2	4	2
1–9	3	0	3	8	11	8
3–9	3	4	7	8	11	4
5–9	0	5	5	11	11	6
5–11	4	5	9	5	9	0
5–15	6	5	11	7	13	2
7–11	5	2	7	4	9	2
9–15	2	7	9	11	13	4
11–15	4	9	13	9	13	0

$LF - EF = 8 - 4 = 4$. Each activity is thus calculated and recorded on a tabulation sheet. (See Table 2–1.)

Construction Schedule. From the data on the tabulation sheet, a construction schedule may now be developed as follows:

1. List the activity numbers of the project on a schedule form.
2. Make a trial schedule, bracketing the *ES* and *LF* time spans.
3. Add the crew size needed.
4. Verify the network logic and show the crew size required.

In making up the schedule, one should identify the *free float* and *interfering float* for each activity. Recall that the total float $TF = LS - ES = LF - EF$. However, activities cannot always be done anytime within the total float without interfering with other activities. Consider, for example, activity 1–9 of Figure 2–5, which may be placed at several points within the duration of the project, including the two shown in Figure 2–8(a) and (b). In checking the network, we note that the location of activity 1–9 in Figure 2–8(b) shows that it interferes with activity 9–15. (See figure 2–9.) Therefore, activity 1–9 should be finished before the eighth time unit begins. Consequently, the free float for activity 1–9 occurs from the eighth through the eleventh time unit. Interfering float, which is usually shown with Xs, is illustrated in Figure 2–10.

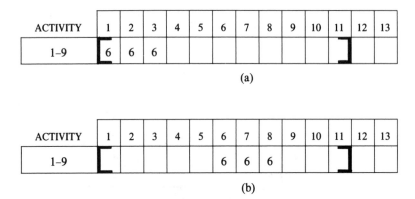

ACTIVITY	1	2	3	4	5	6	7	8	9	10	11	12	13
1–9	6	6	6										

(a)

ACTIVITY	1	2	3	4	5	6	7	8	9	10	11	12	13
1–9						6	6	6					

(b)

Figure 2–8. Activities may be scheduled anywhere within the total float, assuming that they do not interfere with other activities.

All activities must be scheduled to conform to network logic. Also, remember to check dummy activities; they are not shown on the schedule because they do not take time, but they sometimes affect other activities.

Figure 2–11 shows a complete early start schedule with worker requirements added and interfering float noted. Figure 2–12 illustrates another project schedule with activity descriptions added for quick reference, and equipment and labor requirements added as well.

ACTIVITY	1	2	3	4	5	6	7	8	9	10	11	12	13
1–9						6	6	6					
9–15									5	5			

Figure 2–9. In checking the network, we see that the above scheduling will not work because activity 1–9 must be completed before 9–15 can start.

ACTIVITY	1	2	3	4	5	6	7	8	9	10	11	12	13
1–9	6	6	6					X	X	X	X		
9–15								5	5				

Figure 2–10. Schedule with interfering float marked with X's.

DAY

ACTIVITY	1	2	3	4	5	6	7	8	9	10	11	12	13
1–3	4	4	4	4	X	X	X	X					
1–5	5	5	5	5	5								
1–7	4	4	X	X									
1–9	6	6	6					X	X	X	X		
3–9					2	2	2	X	X	X	X		
5–11						7	7	7	7				
5–15						4	4	4	4	4	4		
7–11			3	3	3	3	3						
9–15								5	5				
11–15										8	8	8	8
TOTAL WORKERS	19	19	18	12	10	16	16	16	16	12	12	8	8

Figure 2–11. Complete early start schedule with total number of workers needed and interfering float noted.

ACTIVITY NUMBER	DESCRIPTION	1	2	3	4	5	6	7	8	9	10	11	12	13
1–3	Assemble culvert #1	4	4	4										
1–5	Dig trench #1	1BH/2			X	X	X							
1–7	Dig trench #2		1BH/2											
3–7	Assemble culvert #2				4	4	4							
5–9	Install culvert #1				8	X	X	X						
7–11	Install culvert #2							8						
9–13	Backfill #1					1FL/3								
11–13	Backfill #2							1FL/3						
	Resources:													
	Backhoe (BH)	1	1											
	Workers	6	6	4	12	7	8	3						
	Front loader (FL)					1		1						

Figure 2–12. Sample project schedule with activity descriptions and equipment and labor requirements.

3

EARTHMOVING EQUIPMENT

CRAWLER TRACTORS AND DOZERS

Crawler tractors are essential to many construction projects. In fact, the crawler is perhaps the most used of any construction vehicle. It is available in a wide range of sizes and horsepower ratings and has an equally wide range of special-purpose attachments.

Crawlers are commonly broken into three size/weight classes: light, medium, and heavy. They employ diesel engines, typically with three, four, six, eight, or 12 cylinders and range in horsepower from about 65 to over 700. Typical operating weights range from approximately 15,000 to 174,000 pounds. Power is rated in drawbar pounds pull. (See Figure 3–1.)

The crawler tractor is used where high speed is not possible but high drawbar pounds pull and good traction are mandatory. Crawlers have been used for many purposes, but typically for pushing or pulling heavy loads. They will operate in water and muck as high as the tracks and even deeper with waterproofing equipment. Perhaps the most essential operating characteristic of the crawler tractor is that it is a powerful, versatile machine best used for rough work over short distances. It is not efficient traveling long distances, and transporting such a machine long distances under its own power is a waste of its operational life. Transport trailers should be used to take the crawler long distances.

Attachments

At one time, the straight and angled dozer blade were the prime crawler tractor attachments. Tractors with these blades were the first machines on the job and the last to leave. They performed a multitude of tasks, from clearing very rough land all the way to finish grading work. Even today, the crawler tractor with straight or angled dozer blade sees perhaps more use than any other piece of construction equipment.

Special attachments to the crawler can significantly improve its performance. In land clearing, for example, one manufacturer reports that 30 to 40% more land can be cleared in a given time by using such attachments. The following is a listing of crawler attachments with their general characteristics and uses.

The Straight ("S") Blade. The straight blade continues to be the single most versatile tractor attachment available. It is a good production tool capable of handling heavy material. Equipped with a push plate, it may be used in combination with rubber-tired tractors to push loading scrapers. (See Figure 3-2(a) and (b) .)

(a)

(b)

(c)

Figure 3–1. (a) John Deere light crawler tractor. (b) John Deere medium-class crawler tractor. (c) International-Hough crawler tractor, heavy class.

The Universal ("U") Blade. The universal blade is used for lighter or more easily dozed material than the S blade is used for. The U blade has large "wings" which make it particularly useful for moving large loads. It also finds use in land reclamation, stockpiling, charging hoppers and trapping for loaders, prying, ditching, leveling, and various kinds of utility work. (See Figure 3–2(c).)

The Angling ("A") Blade. The angling blade can be used straight on or angled 25 degrees to either side. The angling capacity reduces the amount of maneuvering the tractor must do in sidecasting, pioneering roads, backfilling, cutting ditches, and similar work. (See Figure 3–2(d).)

The Cushion ("C") Blade. The cushion blade is equipped with impact-resistant rubber cushions that allow the tractor to push a scraper without coming to a complete stop at the scraper push block. It can also be used for other general dozing work. The relatively narrow width of the blade makes it maneuverable in tight spaces. (See Figure 3–2(e).)

The AEM U-Blades. The AEM U-blades move high volumes of light, noncohesive materials (coal, wood chips, etc.). Heavier blades of this type are available for more typical production dozer work. (See Figure 3–2(f).)

The Power Angling and Tilt ("PAT") Blade. The PAT blade may be raised, lowered, tilted, or angled left or right, for functions like grading, backfilling ditches, landscaping, and fill spreading. (See Figure 3-2(g) and (h) .)

The Landfill Blade. The landfill blade is good for handling refuse and cover material, spreading work, and of course landfill. The trash screen at the top of the blade protects the tractor radiator without obscuring the operator's vision. A curved moldboard keeps cover material rolling evenly. (See Figure 3–2(i).)

The K/G Blade. Good for land clearing, the K/G blade can cut trees, pile vegetation, cut v-type drainage ditches, and build woods roads and firebreaks. (See Figure 3–2(j).)

The V-tree Cutter. The v-tree cutter is a special blade that is shaped in a sharp v-angle. Each side of the blade is a sharp cutting edge for shearing trees, stumps, and brush at ground level. Trees or growth fall away at the sides of the blade. (See Figure 3-2(k), (1), (m).)

The Rake Blade. The rake blade is designed for land clearing work. It handles vegetation up to tree size and removes small stumps, rocks, and roots. There are several rake blade configurations. (See Figure 3-2(n).)

The Clamp Rake. The clamp rake does the work of the land clearing rake but is equipped with hydraulically operated clamps that can pick up and carry trees, stumps, boulders, etc. (See Figure 3–3.)

Source: International-Hough   (a)

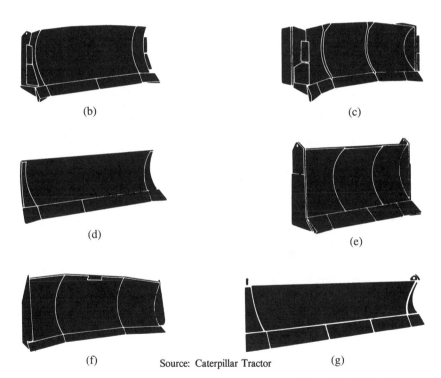

(b)   (c)

(d)   (e)

(f)   Source: Caterpillar Tractor   (g)

Figure 3–2. (a) International-Hough crawler tractor with straight blade. (b) Straight (''S'') blade. (c) Universal (''U'') blade. (d) Angling (''A'') blade. (e) Cushion (''C'') blade. (f) AEM U-blades. (g) Power angling and tilt (''PAT'') blade.

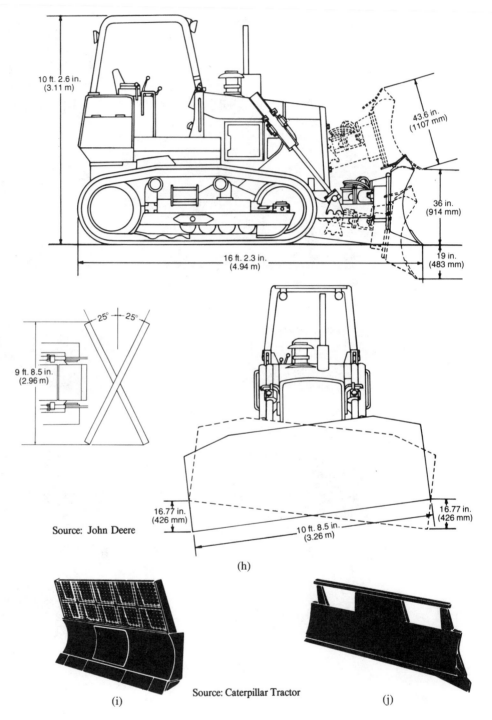

Source: John Deere

(h)

Source: Caterpillar Tractor

(i)

(j)

Figure 3-2 (Continued). (h) John Deere All-Hydraulic Dozer with power angling and tilt blade. Note the blade tilts to either side and may be angled up to 25 degrees as shown. (i) Landfill flade. (j) K/G blade.

(k)

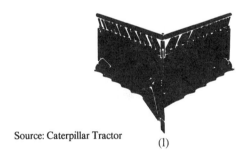

Source: Caterpillar Tractor

(l)

Figure 3–2 (Continued). (k) Caterpillar D8L tractor with Rome K/G blade. (l) V-tree cutter.

(m)

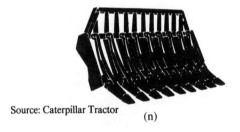

Source: Caterpillar Tractor (n)

Figure 3–2 (Continued). (m) Caterpillar D8L crawler tractor with Rome V-tree cutter. (n) Rake blade.

Root Plows. The root plow is designed to kill brush and growth by undercutting at the crown or bud ring. Large roots are thereby forced to the surface. Root plows are also used to shatter hard surface crusts and hardpan.

Root plows are chiefly used in land clearing. They are built with a rear trunnion-mounted frame with a horizontally mounted knife-type moldboard. Large "fins" are welded to the blade, whose angle may be adjusted to suit the difficulty of the material. The moldboard is pulled through the ground by the tractor at a depth of about eight to 18 inches. (See Figure 3–4.)

Source: Caterpillar Tractor

Figure 3–3. FLECO 977L clamp rake.

Figure 3–4. Rome/Holt root plow with over-the-cab hydraulics.

Source: Caterpillar Tractor

Figure 3–5. FLECO D7G rolling chopper.

Rolling Choppers. The rolling chopper is a steel drum with cutting blades welded on. The drum is usually filled with water to increase its weight. Rolling choppers are towed behind tractors, and as they turn, they fracture and shatter undesirable low growth, penetrating to about six to 10 inches deep. Multiple drums may be used if necessary. These choppers destroy low growth with a minimum of damage to topsoil.

Typical uses of rolling choppers include preparation of forest sites, brush control on right-of-ways, clearing for reservoirs, maintenance, and similar tasks. (See Figure 3–5.)

The Hydraulic Tree Shear. The hydraulic tree shear uses hydraulic power and shear blades to prune whole trees at ground level. It quickly fells (less than one minute each) softwood trees up to 30 inches and hardwood trees up to 22 inches in diameter. This equipment has been used primarily for harvesting pulpwood. However, its ability to work in tight spaces makes it good for thinning and selectively removing trees from residential development sites or any place where similar work will be done. (See Figure 3–6.)

Chains. Chains are usually used in large lengths (about 300 feet of 2½-inch anchor chain) that are dragged behind two crawler tractors, primarily for land clearing. Depending on the size of the chains and tractors, fairly large trees can be felled. However, for best operation, the trees to be felled should

Source: Caterpillar Tractor

Figure 3–6. FLECO 931B tree shear.

be no more than 18 inches in diameter and of a density of 1,000 or fewer trees per acre. Heavy undergrowth is a great hindrance to chaining.

Rippers. Rear-mounted hydraulically operated rippers are frequently used with crawler tractors. Rippers are available in several configurations and they typically have from one to five shanks or "teeth." These shanks point downward and angle toward the front of the tractor so that they are pulled down into the soil and under objects to be removed. Often, rock may be ripped, as well as old asphalt, concrete, masonry, and similar materials and obstacles.(See Figure 3–7.)

Wheel-mounted towed rippers are available but are used less frequently than tractor-mounted rippers. For very heavy ripping, a towed ripper may be pulled by one tractor and pushed by another. This is expensive, but usually less expensive than a blasting and hauling operation to accomplish the same task.

Other special-purpose attachments. Special-purpose attachments other than the ones just discussed exist to speed up certain segments of the overall job. In some cases it will be economical for a contractor to purchase one or more of them; in other cases it will be more cost effective to rent or lease them. Each contractor's situation will be somewhat different. However, every contractor should be able to estimate the production and profit gained by any piece of equipment to determine the best of the following courses:

RIPPER SPECIFICATIONS

Type .... **Multi-Shank**

Tool Beam
  Overall Width .... 97" (2464 mm)
  Cross Section, height x width .... 15" x 18.8" (381 x 478 mm)
  Ground Clearance under tool beam:
    Ripper raised .... 64.8" (1646 mm)
    Ripper lowered .... 12.5" (316 mm)

Shank
  · Number of Shanks per ripper, max. 3
  Spacing center to center .... 42.0" (1067 mm)
  Penetration, max. .... 28.2" (716 mm)
  Ground Clearance, max. raised .... 33.5" (851 mm)
  Shank Positions (vertical) 2

Weight
  Complete, including one shank .... 10 580 lb (4800 kg)
  Each additional shank .... 700 lb (320 kg)

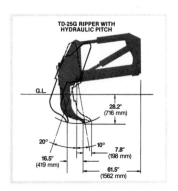

(a)

(b)

Figure 3–7. (a) Rippers increase the efficiency of dozer and other blades by loosening and ripping up obtacles such as rock, concrete, asphalt, and roots. (b) Caterpillar D10 tractor with rear-mounted hydraulic ripper. This mammoth machine weighs 174,200 lb and develops 700 hp.

1. Spend extra time with the equipment on hand.
2. Rent or lease special attachments.
3. Purchase special attachments where their profitable use is assured.

RUBBER-TIRED TRACTORS

The rubber-tired tractor is used for essentially the same purpose as the crawler tractor. However, it performs earthmoving operations faster and thus more economically than both crawler tractors working with scrapers and shovel-and-truck operations. And, like the crawler, it can tow earthhauling scrapers, trailers, rippers, etc. Thus, where it can be done, the rubber-tired tractor should be used instead of the crawler, because of its advantage in speed. (See Figure 3–8.)

The main disadvantage of the rubber-tired tractor relative to the crawler is that it has less traction. Wide tires and four-wheel drive improve traction, but still, the vehicle cannot attain the traction of a crawler. Thus, in rough work where high traction is essential, the crawler is the machine of choice. Note also that the relatively high bearing pressure of the rubber-tired tractor reduces its performance as well.

Where site conditions permit, rubber-tired tractors can travel at relatively high speeds while towing their payload. Rubber-tired tractors are rated in pounds rimpull of pulling force. *Rimpull* is the tractive force between the driving tires and the travel surface.

Despite its tractional difficulties in most rough-site situations, the rubber-tired tractor has better traction than the crawler on surfaced areas (such as concrete or asphalt) because the crawler treads tend to slip on hard surfaces. Available traction is influenced both by the coefficient of friction between the drive wheels and the travel surface and by the amount of weight on the drive wheels. Thus, the weight to be hauled and the type of surface the material will be moved over are factors in determining whether or not a rubber-tired tractor should be considered for a particular job. Other factors such as type of tires and drive (two-wheel, four-wheel, etc.) also affect the selection of the right machine for the job.

In summary, the rubber-tired tractor has a speed advantage over the crawler; requires less transportation equipment because it can travel considerable distances under its own power; has good traction on existing hard surfaces such as concrete and asphalt (and will not damage those surfaces, as will the crawler); and, because of its high ground bearing pressure, compacts materials. Thus, where site conditions permit (and otherwise, as soon as possible), the rubber-tired tractor is chosen over the crawler.

(a)

(b)

Figure 3–8. (a) Clark rubber-tired tractor with log grapple. (b) Clark rubber-tired tractor with coal blade.

SCRAPERS

Scrapers are used in earthmoving to self-load, haul, and dump. The scraper is essentially a large steel bowl with a cutting edge at the front. The cutting edge may be either a type of blade or a ladder-type elevator that lifts the earth up as the vehicle moves. The bowl itself may be angled up or down, and this movement determines the depth of the cut. The type of material being gathered is a strong factor in determining the depth of cut that can be made. Typically, loads are dumped out the back or bottom (or both) of the bowl. To operate the bowl, scrapers may utilize either cables operated by the towing unit or hydraulic power. The towing unit may be a crawler tractor or a rubber-tired tractor. However, the tendency nowadays is toward towing units specially designed for the particular scraper. Hydraulic power from the towing unit is typical. (See Figure 3–9.)

(a)

Figure 3–9. (a) Caterpillar standard (not elevating) tandem-powered, push–pull scraper. Elevating scrapers in single and tandem power also available.

(b)

(c)

Figure 3–9 (Continued). (b) John Deere elevating scraper. (c) John Deere elevating scraper. Note turning radius.

Scraper capacities vary from about nine to 22 cubic yards struck, from about 20 to 44 cubic yards heaped. *Struck* means that the bowl or carrying unit has a full load of material that is level with its top. *Heaped* means that the carrying unit is heaped with all the material it can hold without the material's falling off.

Operating ranges for scrapers vary depending on the vehicle that tows them. Crawler tractors would be used for towing over relatively short distances, say, from 300 to 1200 feet. (See Figure 3–10.) For distances under 300 feet the dozer would usually be used. For distances beyond 1200 feet, the crawler would ordinarily be too slow and the rubber-tired tractor would be the towing unit. However, as mentioned previously, the tendency in scrapers is toward specially designed tow vehicles, vehicles designed for the specific scraper, and these modern vehicles can travel longer distances than crawler/scraper or rubber-tired tractor/scraper combinations at higher speeds with just as large payloads.

The Scraper Work Cycle

The scraper work cycle may be broken into three operations: loading, hauling, and spreading.

Loading. Several suggestions for loading are:

Figure 3–10. Caterpillar D8L tractor pulling Rome scraper.

1. Make use of gravity by loading downhill where practicable.

2. Straddle-load. Straddle loading is done by cutting a full strip and then leaving an "island" somewhat less than a full cut before the next full cut. The island then is easier to load than a full cut. Straddle loading is frequently done with two or more scrapers operating at once.

3. Avoid tire spinning by pushing towed or self-propelled scrapers with crawlers or rubber-tired tractors. Push–pull wheel tractor–scrapers with two engines, one at each end of the scraper, may also be used.

4. Load as quickly as possible. To do so requires the deepest cut possible at the best speed, which often means that push assistance is needed. Generally, the scraper should be filled in less than 1 minute in about 100 feet of distance.

5. Use the best equipment and the best operators in the borrow pit. Control traffic carefully and get the loads out as quickly as possible.

6. Enter the loading area at the highest safe speed and begin loading as soon as possible.

7. Supervise cuts in the borrow pit, maintaining good drainage. This makes it possible to work in wetter weather. Similarly, slope access roads so that they will drain.

8. Remove obstacles from the loading area; root and rip, if necessary, to maximize efficiency of the scrapers.

Hauling. Hauling involves carrying the load of material to its destination and then returning empty for another load. In production estimation calculations, haul time is often referred to as travel time, which is broken into haul time (time loaded and moving) plus return time (time empty and returning for more material).

Some suggested hauling techniques are:

1. Lay out haul roads to ensure the least travel time. This usually means taking the shortest, straightest routes possible unless severe grades or other obstacles make longer routes necessary.

2. Make turns on the shortest radius possible at the highest safe speed (the highest gear possible).

3. Keep equipment running as closely together as safety will allow. Keep slower equipment on separate routes from those of faster equipment if practicable.

4. Reduce dust by sprinkling roads.

Spreading. Spreading is the term used to denote the filling in of the desired location with material. Some suggested spreading techniques are:

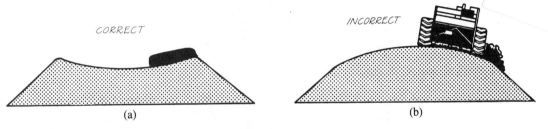

Figure 3–11. (a) Fill slopes should be built up from the outside edges, working toward the center. This keeps the scraper from sliding off the edge, making for more accurate slopes. Drainage precautions must be taken to prevent ponding in the center. (b) Slopes built from the center out tend to lose fill material off the edges. Also, the scraper is difficult to keep in position. Accurate degree of slope is difficult or impossible to maintain.

1. Route scrapers so that they aid in compaction by spreading loads at the beginning of the fill area. Each scraper will then travel over the previous fill to get to the next one. This method will cut down on the time required for the operation of compaction equipment.

2. Spread in the highest gear at the highest safe speed without lugging gears.

3. Keep fill higher on the outside edges of the fill area. (See Figure 3–11.)

MOTOR GRADERS

Motor graders are familiar machines to almost everyone, perhaps because, in addition to doing general construction work, they are frequently used to maintain existing public roads and streets. (See Figure 3–12.) Graders are used primarily for the following types of work:

1. Grading and shaping surfaces.

2. Ditching and bank sloping.

3. Maintaining roads, runways, parking lots, and similar surfaces.

4. Leveling and crowning roads, parking lots, etc.; light planing of irregular surfaces.

5. Light soil stripping (not excavation).

6. Light spreading of loose fill.

(a)

(b)

Figure 3–12. (a) Caterpillar 12G motor grader. (b) John Deere 772A motor grader. Note ripper on front and rear.

7. Backfilling ditches.

8. Snow removal.

9. Scarifying operations (breaking up certain hard soils, asphalt, pavement, etc.).

Motor graders range from about 125 to 250 horsepower, with operating weights of approximately 26,000 to 50,000 pounds and more. Their capabilities (essentially, the amount and type of material they can handle and their ground speed) vary, depending on their power, weight, the type of blade they have, any special attachments there are, etc.

The grader uses a moldboard similar in appearance to a wide dozer blade. However, the grader blade is more concave than the dozer blade and thus rolls the load more, which is helpful in spreading material. A grader is *not* intended to do dozer work. Graders cut ditches to about 3 feet in progressive passes and, in general, are used for lighter, shallower cuts than dozer work entails. Obviously, the harder the soil or other material, the more restricted is the use of motor graders.

The grader blade is adjusted hydraulically. Many positions of the blade are possible, including vertical, and the pitch of the blades may be varied so that the blade cuts or drags material. Thus, the grader is quite versatile in the relatively light work it performs.

Several suggested grader techniques are:

1. Minimize the number of turns the grader makes. For short passes (less than 1,000 feet), it is more efficient to back the grader to the starting point than to turn around at the end and head back to the starting point.

2. Minimize the number of passes needed to do the job.

3. Keep the tires inflated as per the manufacturer's recommendations for the particular job.

4. Where road work is being done on roads currently in operation, plan to work one side of the road at a time, thus reducing shutdown time for the road. Increase the number of graders to minimize the number of passes and speed up the job.

5. On long passes where turns are difficult at the end, grade in reverse on the return pass.

4

COMPACTION EQUIPMENT

SOIL COMPACTION

Compacting soil increases its density, making it stronger and more stable, and thus more able to support loads. Soil compaction is largely affected by (1) material gradation, (2) moisture content, and (3) compactive effort.

Material Gradation. Material gradation has to do with the particle sizes and the percentage of the sizes that are present within a given soil sample. A good soil (one that is capable of being well compacted) will contain a variety of particle sizes, the percentage of sizes, one to another, being the chief factor in promoting compaction. During compaction, the smaller particles will be worked between and around the larger particles, reducing the percentage of voids in the soil (i.e., reducing the distance between particles), thus making the soil denser and stronger.

Poor soil (soil that is difficult to compact or soil that cannot be compacted) contains a high percentage of similar-sized particles and/or a poor relationship of the percentage of sizes to one another. In such soil, a relatively high percentage of voids remains after compaction and the soil lacks density and strength. (See Figure 4–1.)

Moisture Content. Soils are difficult to compact when they are too dry or too wet. Consider, for example, trying to compact dust or mud: it is intuitively obvious that these materials cannot be compacted. What is not so obvious is what the *optimum moisture content* for compaction is. The optimum moisture content is that amount of moisture that helps the soil particles slip easily into their most dense, compacted positions for a given amount of compactive effort. But how much moisture is optimum for a given material? The answer to this question is given in a *Proctor curve,* also called a *compaction curve* and a *moisture–density curve.* (See Figure 4–2.)

Compactive Effort. The compactive effort is the method used to compact the soil. A variety of compaction equipment is available that compacts soil by means of one or more of the following methods:

Poorly-graded   Well-graded

Source: Caterpillar Tractor

Figure 4–1. Material gradation. To be well graded, a soil must contain an even distribution of particle sizes.

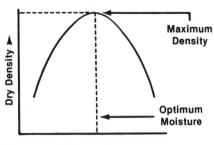

Source: Caterpillar Tractor

Figure 4–2. This curve, called a Proctor curve, compaction curve, or moisture–density curve, shows the relationship between dry density and moisture content.

1. Static weight or pressure
2. Kneading or manipulating action
3. Impact
4. Vibration

Compactor types that utilize the above compaction methods include:

1. Sheepsfoot roller
2. Grid or mesh
3. Vibratory drums, tampers, etc.
4. Steel drum
5. Pneumatic-tired roller
6. Other compactors

Sheepsfoot Roller. The sheepsfoot **and "padded foot" rollers consist of** a drum with tamping feet or protrusions (ergo, *sheepsfoot*) welded on, the drum mounted on a carrying frame. Sheepsfoot rollers may be towed by tractors but are available as self-propelled units. Two or more of them may be connected together. (See Figure 4–3.)

The sheepsfoot roller is designed to knead the soil. When the soil is sufficiently compacted, the "feet" no longer penetrate it and the roller "walks out" (on the top of the soil). If the roller does not walk out, the soil is probably not being compacted because the roller is either too heavy or inappropriate for the soil conditions. Conversely, if the roller does not initially penetrate the soil, then the roller is either too light or otherwise inappropriate for the soil conditions.

Figure 4–3. This padded foot compactor kneads the soil and "walks out" once the feet no longer penetrate the soil.

The sheepsfoot roller is best used for clay or other cohesive soils, not for very sandy, granular, or otherwise noncohesive soils. Sheepsfoot rollers are simple to operate: they are simply pulled back and forth over the soil until they walk out of it.

Some suggested sheepsfoot roller techniques are:

1. Overlap the preceding pass by about 1 foot, thereby assuring that the entire area will be compacted.
2. Avoid sharp turns, which tend to tear up the soil.
3. When compacting against structures, run parallel to the structure if possible. If it is not possible, as in close quarters, pile up fill material about axle high next to the structure, and then back the roller over the fill until the area is compacted.
4. When using the roller to aerate soil, run the machine at the highest safe speed, as high-speed operation tends to tear up the soil for better air exposure.
5. To reduce the danger of compacting the edges of deep fills, use three rollers, compacting by backing only the third roller over the fill. The tractor, and most of the weight, are thus kept away from the edge.

Grid Roller (Mesh). The grid roller operates in a manner similar to that of the sheepsfoot roller. However, the kneading element of the grid roller is a massive grid or mesh, not "feet," as the sheepsfoot roller has. When equipped with extra weight, such as slabs of concrete, this grid can exert tremendous pressure on the soil, crushing rocks and pushing the broken pieces beneath the surface.

Vibratory Compaction Equipment. It is likely that the idea of using vibratory compaction equipment grew out of the simple observation on job sites that vibrating machinery, such as pile drivers, trucks, and other vehicular traffic, tended to consolidate sand and soil near the source of the vibration. Various early design configurations evolved for the vibrating surfaces that made contact with the soil to be compacted.

Nowadays, a vibratory function is available for most of the typical compaction equipment: sheepsfoot rollers, pneumatic-tired rollers, steel drum rollers, etc. Also, various smaller and special-purpose vibratory devices are available in self-propelled and manually operated versions. Vibratory equipment works best on sandy soil, sand, gravel, and in general, soils that are relatively noncohesive.

Steel Drum Compactor. The steel drum compactor is a smooth-wheeled steel roller that is typically water ballasted. It may be towed or self-propelled, and one, two, and three-axle types are common. It is frequently classified by weight, as for example, the two-axle tandem roller (5–8 tons), the three-axle tandem roller (9–14 tons), etc. The lower weight is the minimum, the higher weight the maximum, ballast included.

The two-axle roller is suitable for compacting either diagonally across or lengthwise along surfaces. The three-axle roller should only be used lengthwise. Thus, the two-axle roller sees more general use than the three-axle roller, which is used chiefly on large highway projects, runways, and similar projects.

In general, steel drum compactors are most effective on granular materials such as sand, gravel, and crushed stone. Usually, they are used after deeper compactors have been operating. Steel drum compactors see much use on streets, highways, runways, parking lots, and similar compaction jobs. (See Figure 4–4.) Some suggested operating techniques are:

1. Avoid acceleration, sudden stops, or movements that tend to displace surface materials. Slow, regular speeds are usually required to do the job.
2. Avoid sharp turns.
3. Use (and maintain) a sprinkler system when working hot, tacky material.
4. Do not allow the machine to stand on cooling or setting road surfaces (usually asphalt), or depressions in the surface will result.

Pneumatic-tired Roller. The pneumatic-tired roller utilizes inflatable tires to knead and compact the soil. The number and size of the tires vary, and

(a)

(b)

Figure 4-4. Steel drum compactors are most effective on granular materials such as sand, gravel, crushed stone, asphalt, etc.

Source: Ingersoll-Rand   (c)

Figure 4–4. (Continued).

tire pressures are varied in accordance with different conditions. Large wheels (over 5 feet in outside diameter) roll more easily than smaller tires and require less drawbar pull than do smaller tires. Higher tire pressure causes the tires to sink deeper and compact deeper. However, beginning passes are sometimes made at lesser tire pressures to precompact the soil somewhat, thereby avoiding rutting of the soil. Tire pressures usually range between 90 and 150 pounds per square inch.

Pneumatic rollers may be towed or self-propelled. They range from about 15 to 200 tons gross weight, with a maximum wheel load of about 50 tons. They are available as single- or dual-axle machines, oscillating units with two wheels per axle, or individually loaded wheel units. The tires are arranged for thorough coverage of a given area. Because of the adjustments possible (e.g.,weight, tire diameter, tire pressure), this type of machine can compact a variety of soil types to depths greater than 18 inches in fewer passes than a comparable sheepsfoot roller.

Suggested techniques for using pneumatic-tired rollers are:

1. Adjust passes to compensate for any gaps between the tires. (At least two passes are usually required.)

2. When traveling over existing finished roads, remove ballast to avoid damage to the road.

3. If the tires are filled with water for extra weight, either drain them in cold weather or add an acceptable anti-freeze.

4. Do not allow the unit to bog down in soil. Varying the tire pressure will often help, although it may be necessary to supply push assistance in the form of a tractor or some other pusher.

5. Clear rocky areas and remove other obstructions that may damage the tires.

6. Avoid turns on compacted areas. When turns must be made, make them gradually.

7. Do not overload the rollers. Overloading lessens the kneading action inherent in the roller type of compaction.

8. When compacting steep banks, pull the roller up and down the bank with a dragline.

9. When compacting base and surface courses, work from the outside toward the centerline.

Landfill Compactors. Because of the variations in material, landfill equipment requirements are difficult to assess. Different daily volumes further complicate the job of selecting equipment to spread and compact refuse. Typical equipment includes crawlers, track loaders, wheel loaders, tamping machines, and chopper wheel compactors. (See Figure 4–5.)

The most common materials found in residential landfills include paper, yard waste, food waste, and miscellaneous materials. Table 4–1 gives the proportions of typical waste materials by weight. Fortunately, landfill operations

Source: John Deere

Figure 4–5. Landfill compactor with chopper wheels and special blade.

Table 4–1. Typical landfill materials.

Composition of Refuse

The main landfill material of most communities consists of residential and commercial refuse in the following proportions by weight:

Paper 31%
Yard waste 19%
Food waste 18%
Glass 10%
Metal 10%
Wood 4%
Plastic 3%
Rubber & leather 3%
Misc. inorganics 1%
Textiles 1%

are not usually under the time pressures normally associated with general construction work. Thus, more time is available for experimentation in moving and compacting the material of a particular community and for the gradual assembly of the appropriate fleet of equipment.

Other Compactors. Various smaller compactors exist for use in close quarters or for special uses. These compactors are available with gasoline engines, electric engines, or air power.

Truck-mounted Water Distributor

For the purposes of this text, the principal use of the water distributor is the application of water to the subgrade to aid in compaction. Other uses include dust control and firefighting.

The truck-mounted water distributor consists of a tank (1,000-gallon capacity is common), pumping system, spraybar assembly, instruments, and other equipment aiding the controlled distribution of water. Water distributors work ahead of compaction equipment where moisture is needed to aid compaction. The chief controlling factors in water distribution are available pumping pressure, truck speed, and spraybar length. (Twenty-four foot widths are common, but greater or smaller widths for special uses also exist.)

5

TRENCHING EQUIPMENT

Trenching machines, also called ditchers or trenchers, are used for digging trenches for (1) water, gas, and oil lines, (2) telephone cable lines, (3) sewer lines, (4) drainage ditches, and (5) other similar underground items and endeavors. The size and type of machine selected for a particular job depends on the size and depth of the trench needed and on soil, site, and other conditions. Trenchers are available that will dig any type of soil except solid rock.

Trenchers typically utilize rotating wheels over which cutting buckets, digging chains, or similar digging devices move continuously. The digging apparatus is simply lowered to the desired depth as the carrier moves along the trench line.

Carriers for trenchers are often custom built for the particular machine, although crawler tractors, rubber-tired tractors, trucks, or ordinary farm tractors may be the carrier vehicle. The type of trencher and carrier selected, of course, depends on the requirements of the job. Production capability varies widely. (See Figure 5–1.)

(a)

Figure 5–1. Many sizes and configurations of trenchers are available to meet particular job needs.

(b)

(c)

Figure 5–1. (Continued).

Source: Vermeer   (d)

Source: Vermeer   (e)

Figure 5–1. (Continued).

Source: Vermeer   (f)

Figure 5–1. (Continued).

Backhoe. A general discussion of the backhoe will be found in Chapter 6, on excavating equipment. In addition to doing excavation work, the backhoe is an excellent trencher. It can dig well below the tracks or wheels of the carrier in most materials, soft or hard. Various size dippers are available to match the desired trench width. (See Figure 5–2.)

Some suggested backhoe trenching techniques are:

1. Select the dipper to match the trench width rather than making additional passes with a smaller dipper.
2. Keep the backhoe centered over the trench.
3. The best production is gained when the dipper is at right angles to the boom.
4. The backhoe will dig hard materials—even rock—once the surface is broken. Break especially hard surfaces with more suitable equipment to save time. Remove particularly hard materials in relatively shallow layers.
5. For ordinary digging, make the cut so that each pass results in a full dipper.

Source: FMC   (a)

Source: Koehring   (b)

Figure 5–2. (a) The backhoe is an excellent trencher. From the same position, this machine is digging trenches for two sizes of pipe and will later
lower the pipe into the trenches. (b) Many sizes and configurations of
backhoes are available. This relatively small machine can handle a wide
range of trenching jobs.

6

EXCAVATING EQUIPMENT

THE CRANE

One of the first pieces of power construction equipment was the crane. It is still one of the most widely used. The crane has changed much over the years and its uses have increased, but its basic operating components remain the same in principle. Those components are (1) the mounting, (2) the deck and cab, and (3) the boom. (See Figure 6–1.)

Each of the components varies in size and configuration to perform different functions. The deck and cab sit on the mounting, which may be crawler tracks, rubber tires, or some other medium. The boom may be one piece, may be equipped with a dipper stick, or may operate like a telescope. The crane itself may be cable operated, hydraulically operated, or may use a combination of cable and hydraulic systems.

To the basic components just listed are added the following six essential attachments which give the crane its lifting and loading abilities, and which give rise to the various names the crane goes by (see Figure 6–2):

1. Hook (lift crane, crane boom)
2. Clamshell
3. Dragline
4. Shovel
5. Backhoe
6. Piledriver

Since each of the attachments has fairly specific uses that it performs best, the crane tends to be called by whatever attachment is being used. Thus, if a crane is using a dragline, the crane is called a dragline, and similarly for

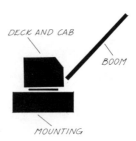

Figure 6–1. The essential components of the crane are (1) the deck and cab, (2) the mounting, and (3) the boom. Each of these components has evolved considerably over the years, but the engineering principles remain about the same.

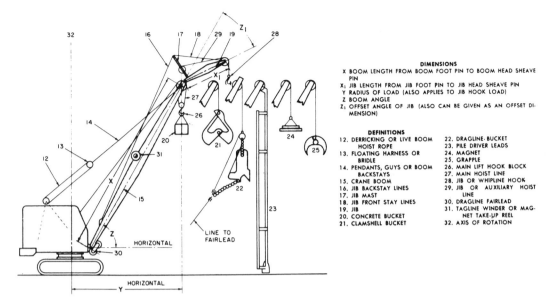

DIMENSIONS

X BOOM LENGTH FROM BOOM FOOT PIN TO BOOM HEAD SHEAVE
  PIN
X_1 JIB LENGTH FROM JIB FOOT PIN TO JIB HEAD SHEAVE PIN
Y RADIUS OF LOAD (ALSO APPLIES TO JIB HOOK LOAD)
Z BOOM ANGLE
Z_1 OFFSET ANGLE OF JIB (ALSO CAN BE GIVEN AS AN OFFSET DI-
  MENSION)

DEFINITIONS

12. DERRICKING OR LIVE BOOM HOIST ROPE	22. DRAGLINE-BUCKET
13. FLOATING HARNESS OR BRIDLE	23. PILE DRIVER LEADS
14. PENDANTS, GUYS OR BOOM BACKSTAYS	24. MAGNET
15. CRANE BOOM	25. GRAPPLE
16. JIB BACKSTAY LINES	26. MAIN LIFT HOOK BLOCK
17. JIB MAST	27. MAIN HOIST LINE
18. JIB FRONT STAY LINES	28. JIB OR WHIPLINE HOOK
19. JIB	29. JIB OR AUXILIARY HOIST LINE
20. CONCRETE BUCKET	30. DRAGLINE FAIRLEAD
21. CLAMSHELL BUCKET	31. TAGLINE WINDER OR MAG-NET TAKE-UP REEL
	32. AXIS OF ROTATION

Figure 6–2. The crane tends to be called by the attachment that is being used. There are many attachments, the most essential of which are the hook, clamshell, dragline, shovel, backhoe, and piledriver. Source: Power Crane and Shovel Association.

when it uses the other attachments. An examination of each of the components of and attachments to the crane follows.

Mounting. As previously mentioned, the crane mounting may be crawler tracks, rubber tires, or another medium. Crawlers work best on terrain too soft or rugged, or otherwise unsuitable for rubber tires.

Crawler tracks are available in different widths and track configurations. Flat tracks are preferred where the terrain is smooth and stable. Also, flat tracks do less damage to streets, runways, and similar paved areas whose surfaces are usually desired to be kept intact. Grouser treads (treads with raised sections) are used in soft soil and, in general, in conditions where greater traction is needed. Wide tracks improve flotation, but managers avoid using them where practicable because wide tracks wear faster than narrow ones.

Rubber-tired Mountings. There are two general types of rubber-tired mountings: the self-propelled single-engine mounting, and the wheel carrier mounting. Self-propelled single-engine mountings use a single engine to propel the unit and to operate the attached equipment. (See Figure 6–3.) The wheel carrier mounting is usually a truck, although towed wheel trailers may be used. Wheel carrier units may use one engine both to propel the carrier and to operate the crane equipment, or they may have two engines, one to propel the carrier and one to operate the crane equipment. (See Figure 6–4.)

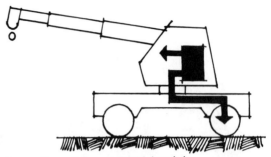

Source: Power Crane and Shovel Association

(a)

Source: FMC

(b)

Figure 6–3. The self-propelled single-engine mounting uses a single engine
to propel the unit and operate the attached equipment.

Wheel carrier drives typically use automotive nomenclature: two axles
with only the rear axle driven is a four-by-two; two axles with both front and
rear axles driven is a four-by-four; three axles with the two rear axles driven
is a six-by-four, etc. The first number is the total number of wheels; the second
is the number of wheels with power. (Dual tires count as one wheel.)

The advantage of rubber tires over tracks is speed of movement. Self-
propelled single-engine mountings are good for moving equipment more rap-

Source: FMC

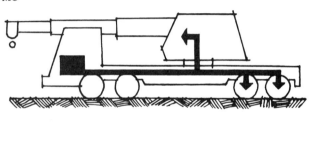

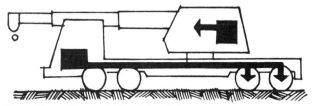

Source: Power Crane and Shovel Association

Figure 6–4. Wheel units may use one engine to propel the carrier and operate crane and attachments, or two engines may be used, one for propelling the carrier and one for the crane and attachments.

idly than crawler tracks over greater distances. Wheeled carriers can travel from job to job at highway speeds.

In summary, rubber-tired mountings are useful where (1) on-site and/or job-to-job mobility and speed are important, and (2) the operation of crawlers would damage pavements or otherwise be impractical.

Deck and Cab. The deck (also called the turntable) is secured to the mounting and typically rotates 360 degrees. The cab, in addition to housing and protecting the operator, contains various devices that supply operational data and aids, for example, load indication, boom angle indication, radius indication, boom length indication, load moment systems, and other operational and safety equipment.

Boom. The boom is an essential lifting and swinging device of the crane. Booms may be raised and lowered from the point of attachment at the deck by cable, by hydraulic power, or by both. Work performed using only the boom is called *boom derricking or lowering.* (See Figure 6–5.)

With the addition of a *dipper stick*, the crane may be equipped with front-end attachments that increase its uses. But regardless of the sizes, configurations, and attachments of the various cranes, their general purpose is the

Figure 6–5. The boom is the essential lifting and swinging component of the crane. Source: Power Crane and Shovel Association.

same: to lift and move earth, materials, supplies, or other loads from one location to another. Following is a discussion of the attachments and their uses.

Lift Cranes. Lift cranes are also called *crane booms* or just *hooks*. The lift crane consists of the crane boom, hoist cables and/or hydraulic equipment, and the hook block. Its basic function is to lift and move some object to a new location by way of a line from the hook block to the object. This objective is usually accomplished by swinging the revolving deck around, but sometimes it may be necessary to move the entire crane unit. (See Figure 6–6.)

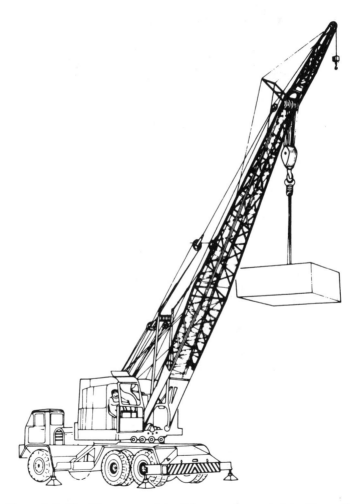

Figure 6–6. The lift crane consists of the crane boom, hoist cables and/or hydraulic equipment, and the hook block.

Source: American Hoist & Derrick Co.

Figure 6–7. Lattice booms typically use two sections attached at the middle. This boom has an additional section in the middle to increase its range. Extensions may also be added at the boom tip.

Although the hook block is the basic attachment of the lift crane, draglines, clamshells, and various other attachments may be used.

The hook block and the boom—especially the long boom used for dragline and similar operations—are frequently lifted by cable. However, hydraulic assistance is sometimes employed.

Booms, which typically consist of two lattice-type sections attached together at the center, may be lengthened by adding sections to the middle or by adding a boom extension or jib at the boom tip. (See Figure 6–7.)

Hydraulic Lift Cranes. In addition to lattice boom-type lift cranes, various hydraulic lift cranes are much used nowadays. (See Figure 6–8.) All lifting crane operations may be divided into three broad categories:

1. *High work,* which takes place well above ground, e.g., lifting supplies, equipment, and materials to high-rise floors, lifting structural members to high places, etc.

2. *Ground-level work,* e.g., unloading trailers and rail cars, swinging lumber from one location to another, etc.

3. *Below-ground-level work,* e.g., lowering concrete buckets to foundation excavations, lowering reinforcing steel, laying pipe, etc.

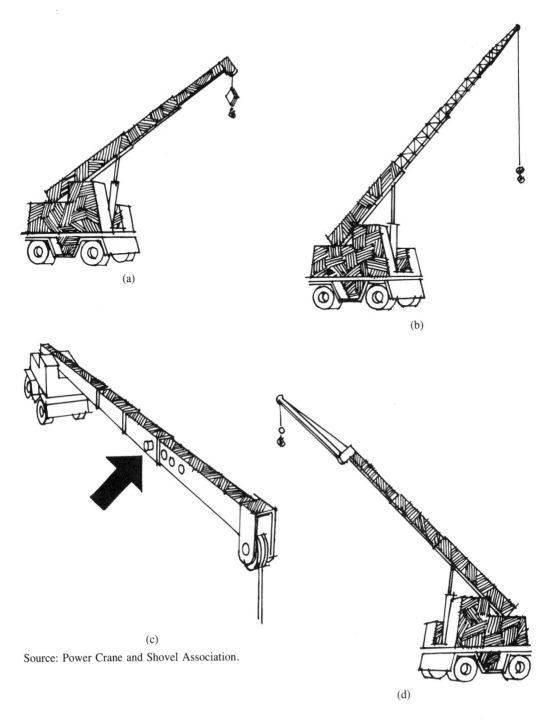

(a)

(b)

(c)

Source: Power Crane and Shovel Association.

(d)

Figure 6–8. Hydraulic lift cranes are available with several boom variations, including (a) the power telescope, (b) telescoping lattice boom, (c) power with manual extension, and (d) a stationary boom tip extension (jib).

Source: American Hoist & Derrick Co.

Figure 6–9. Typical clamshell operation. The clamshell may also be used with hydraulic telescoping booms.

Clamshells. Clamshell equipment includes the crane boom, hoist drum laggings, the clamshell bucket itself, the tagline, and other needed cables. The clamshell bucket is made up of two scoops hinged together, with counterweights secured around the hinge. Both lattice-type cable booms and hydraulic telescoping booms are used. (See Figure 6–9.) When dropped, the weight of the bucket penetrates the material to be lifted, and, as the "shells" are drawn together by the closing lines, the material is secured. The bucket is then raised and swung to the dumping point, and the load is released.

Clamshells work best in soft, loose, or medium-hard materials. The clamshell operates downward in a vertical line from the boom point. Therefore, it is best for jobs such as footings, shafts, or other vertical work, for loading and unloading loose materials from railroad cars, bins, etc., and for forming and moving stockpiles of materials such as soil or gravel.

Dragline. The dragline components include the lattice-type boom, dragline bucket, and fairlead assembly. The fairlead guides the cable onto the drum during the loading operation. The hoist cable raises and lowers the bucket. The drag cable pulls the bucket through the material to be excavated. The bucket is then raised and swung to the dump area, and the load is released. (See Figure 6–10.)

(a)

(b)

Figure 6–10. Dragline operations.

Draglines are very versatile for operations at ground level and below. Soft to medium-hard materials are best. The main advantages of the dragline over machines that might be used for the same work are the dragline's long reach (due to the boom) and its "throw" (the casting out of the bucket). Thus, the operating radius of the job can be quite large. (See Figure 6–11.)

Draglines do not have the digging force of shovels or backhoes. Also, the dragline bucket is not heavy enough to penetrate hard materials and tends to tip over when it hits them. However, draglines are excellent for digging and cleaning ditches, dredging rivers and wetlands, sloping embankments, and the like operations.

Shovels. The hydraulic shovel components of the crane include a boom attached to a revolving superstructure on which it pivots, a dipper arm that pivots vertically on the boom, and a dipper or bucket attached to the dipper arm. Figure 6–12 is illustrative. Hydraulic power is prevalent, but cable-operated shovels are still used.

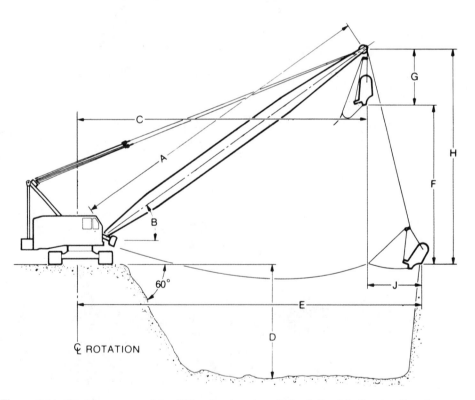

Figure 6–11. Working ranges of the 900 series American Hoist & Derrick Co. dragline. Source: American Hoist & Derrick Co., 63 S. Robert St., St. Paul, MN 55107.

A Boom Length	60 Feet (18.3 M)			70 Feet (21.3 M)			80 Feet (24.4 M)			90 Feet (27.4 M)			100 Feet (30.5 M)		
B Boom Angle	30	35	40	30	35	40	30	35	40	30	35	40	30	35	40
C C/L Rotation To Center Of Dump	(17.4 M) 57'	(16.5 M) 54'	(15.5 M) 51'	(20.1 M) 66'	(18.9 M) 62'	(18.0 M) 59'	(25.6 M) 74'	(21.6 M) 71'	(20.1 M) 66'	(25.3 M) 83'	(24.1 M) 79'	(22.6 M) 74'	(28.0 M) 92'	(26.3 M) 87'	(25.0 M) 82'
D Depth Of Cut (Approx.)	(11.6 M) 38'	(11.6 M) 38'	(11.6 M) 38'	(15.2 M) 50'	(15.2 M) 50'	(15.2 M) 50'	(17.4 M) 57'	(17.4 M) 57'	(17.4 M) 57'	(17.4 M) 57'	(17.4 M) 57'	(17.4 M) 57'	(17.4 M) 57'	(17.4 M) 57'	(17.4 M) 57'
E Digging Reach (Approx.)	(20.1 M) 66'	(19.5 M) 64'	(18.9 M) 62'	(23.5 M) 77'	(22.6 M) 74'	(21.9 M) 72'	(26.2 M) 86'	(25.6 M) 84'	(24.7 M) 81'	(29.3 M) 96'	(28.7 M) 94'	(27.4 M) 90'	(32.3 M) 106'	(31.4 M) 103'	(30.5 M) 100'
F Dumping Height	(4.0 M) 13'	(5.5 M) 18'	(6.7 M) 22'	(5.8 M) 19'	(7.3 M) 24'	(8.8 M) 29'	(7.3 M) 24'	(9.1 M) 30'	(10.7 M) 35'	(8.8 M) 29'	(10.7 M) 35'	(12.8 M) 42'	(10.4 M) 34'	(12.5 M) 41'	(14.6 M) 48'
H Height From Grade To C/L Boom Point	(11.0 M) 36'	(12.5 M) 41'	(13.7 M) 45'	(12.8 M) 42'	(14.3 M) 47'	(15.8 M) 52'	(14.3 M) 47'	(16.2 M) 53'	(17.7 M) 58'	(15.8 M) 52'	(17.7 M) 58'	(19.8 M) 65'	(17.4 M) 57'	(19.5 M) 64'	(21.6 M) 71'
J Casting Distance	(2.7 M) 9'	(3.0 M) 10'	(3.4 M) 11'	(3.4 M) 11'	(3.7 M) 12'	(4.0 M) 13'	(3.7 M) 12'	(4.0 M) 13'	(4.6 M) 15'	(4.0 M) 13'	(4.6 M) 15'	(4.9 M) 16'	(4.3 M) 14'	(4.9 M) 16'	(5.5 M) 18'
Rope Inhauled Length	(31.1 M) 102'	(31.1 M) 102'	(31.1 M) 102'	(32.6 M) 107'	(32.6 M) 107'	(32.6 M) 107'	(34.4 M) 113'	(34.4 M) 113'	(34.4 M) 113'	(36.0 M) 118'	(36.0 M) 118'	(36.0 M) 118'	(36.3 M) 119'	(36.3 M) 119'	(36.3 M) 119'
Rope Hoisted Length	(40.5 M) 133'	(40.5 M) 133'	(40.5 M) 133'	(46.3 M) 152'	(46.3 M) 152'	(46.3 M) 152'	(52.4 M) 172'	(52.4 M) 172'	(52.4 M) 172'	(58.5 M) 192'	(58.5 M) 192'	(58.5 M) 192'	(64.6 M) 212'	(64.6 M) 212'	(64.6 M) 212'

F is based on "G" dimension of 23

Figure 6-11. (Continued).

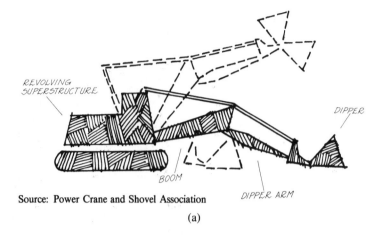

REVOLVING
SUPERSTRUCTURE

DIPPER

BOOM

DIPPER ARM

Source: Power Crane and Shovel Association

(a)

Source: Koehring   (b)

Figure 6–12. (a) The major components of the hydraulic shovel. (b) Hydraulic power is most used.

The movement of the shovel is opposite to that of the backhoe. That is, the bucket moves *away* from the machine into the material, and then upward in a lifting motion. When the bucket is loaded, the revolving superstructure rotates to the dump point and the load is released. (See Figure 6–13.)

Source: Wabco   (c)

Figure 6–12. (Continued). (c) Cable operated shovels are also used.

Shovels are good for excavating materials at the face of embankments and loading such materials onto haul units. Where conditions permit, the treads of the shovel are arranged parallel to the bank. The shovel then faces the bank for excavation, loads the material onto haul units, and proceeds along the embankment. Typical jobs for shovels include excavating road beds, hillside and/ or mountainous work, and digging gravel and sand pits. (See Figure 6–14.)

Backhoe. The major components of the hydraulic backhoe are the revolving superstructure, the boom, the dipper stick or "arm," and the dipper. Cable-operated backhoes are also used, but less frequently than hydraulic machines on most construction sites. (See Figure 6–15.)

In operation, all backhoes dig by first extending the boom and dipper, and then pulling the dipper down and toward the machine. If the material being dug is hard, the dipper may be dragged across the surface at first, and then steadily worked down deeper below ground. The digging cycle continues in this manner, and the depth is limited only by the length of the boom and dipper stick assembly. As material is lifted up, the revolving superstructure rotates, the dipper is swung to the desired point, and the material is released. (See Figures 6–16 and 6–17.)

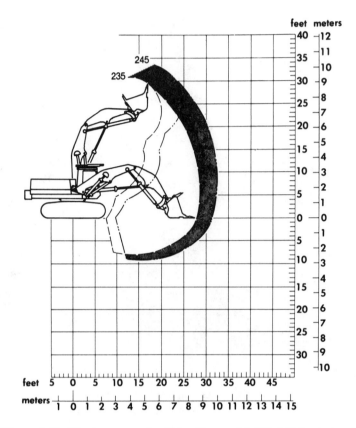

Figure 6–13. Digging ranges for Caterpillar model 235–245 front shovel excavators. Source: Caterpillar.

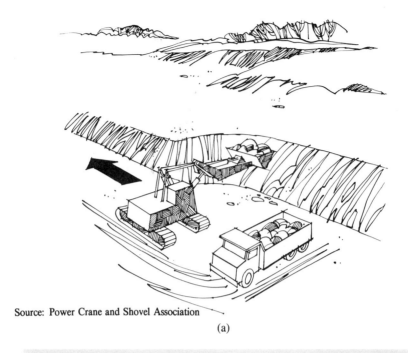

Source: Power Crane and Shovel Association

(a)

Source: Koehring

(b)

Figure 6–14. (a) The shovel works best against banks, facing the bank with the treads or wheels parallel to the bank. (b) and (c) Shovels are good for excavating materials at the face of embankments.

Source: Koehring

(c)

Figure 6–14. (Continued).

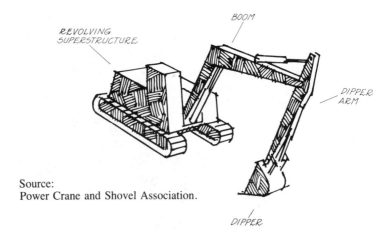

Source:
Power Crane and Shovel Association.

Figure 6–15. The major components of the hydraulic backhoe.

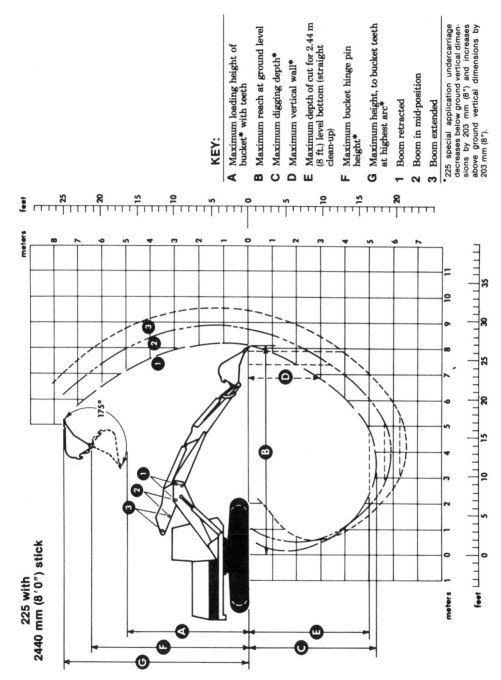

225 with 2440 mm (8′0″) stick

KEY:

A Maximum loading height of bucket* with teeth

B Maximum reach at ground level

C Maximum digging depth*

D Maximum vertical wall*

E Maximum depth of cut for 2.44 m (8 ft.) level bottom (straight clean-up)

F Maximum bucket hinge pin height*

G Maximum height, to bucket teeth at highest arc*

1 Boom retracted

2 Boom in mid-position

3 Boom extended

*225 special application undercarriage decreases below ground vertical dimensions by 203 mm (8″) and increases above ground vertical dimensions by 203 mm (8″).

Figure 6–16. Backhoes dig by first extending the boom and dipper arm, and then pulling the dipper down and toward the machine. As material is lifted up, the revolving superstructure rotates to a desired point and the load is released. Shown: Caterpillar 225 excavator. Source: Caterpillar.

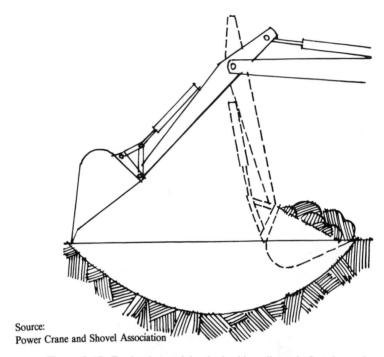

Source:
Power Crane and Shovel Association

Figure 6–17. For hard materials, the backhoe dipper is first dragged across the surface, and then worked deeper.

There is an almost limitless range of sizes of backhoes, from hoes mounted on small agricultural tractors used in residential construction all the way up to huge crawler-mounted hoes capable of handling some of the heaviest work in industrial jobs. (See Figure 6–18.)

Typical attachments for the backhoe include:

1. *Standard dipper*. This dipper is used for regular excavating and trenching. Teeth at the front of the dipper are usually replaceable, extending the life of the dipper. A wide range of dipper sizes is available. The *heavy-duty rock dipper* is basically the same as the standard dipper but is reinforced to deal with harder materials. It, too, has replaceable teeth.

2. *Cleanout dipper*. This dipper is wider than the standard and heavy-duty dippers and has no teeth. As the name implies, it is designed for cleanout work, not regular digging. Clearing loose soil and materials from trenches, pits, etc., are typical uses.

3. *Ripper*. The ripper is a fang-like heavy metal attachment that replaces the other dippers to rip up asphalt, loosen rock, rip frozen earth, etc., prior to regular digging operations.

Source: FMC
(a)

Source: Caterpillar Tractor
(b)

Figure 6–18. Backhoes are one of the most versatile machines in construction use. Particularly useful for trenching, footing, and basement excavation, they also overlap the functions of other machines such as loaders, shovels, scrapers, clamshells, and draglines.

Source: FMC   (c)

Source: John Deere   (d)

Figure 6–18. (Continued).

Source: FMC   (e)

Source: FMC   (f)

Figure 6–18. (Continued).

Source: Koehring

(g)

Figure 6–18. (Continued).

4. *Clamshell*. Typical jobs where the clamshell would be selected over the standard dipper include working around shoring and lateral pipes; excavating manholes, pilings, and footings and other deep vertical work; material handling and loading; cleaning up unwieldy materials (demolition cleanup, mixed materials, etc.); dredging; and aggregate handling. (See Figure 6–19.)

The work functions of the backhoe often overlap those of other machines such as front-end loaders, tractor–shovels, scrapers, clamshells, and draglines. The backhoe is particularly useful for trenching, foundation footing excavation, basement excavation, and similar work. Thus, it is a very versatile machine, almost as common on construction sites as is the pickup truck.

THE TELESCOPING BOOM EXCAVATOR AND CRANE

The major components of the telescoping boom excavator and crane are the hydraulic boom—which extends like a telescope—and whatever attachment is used. The latter is often the hook, in which case the machine operates as a

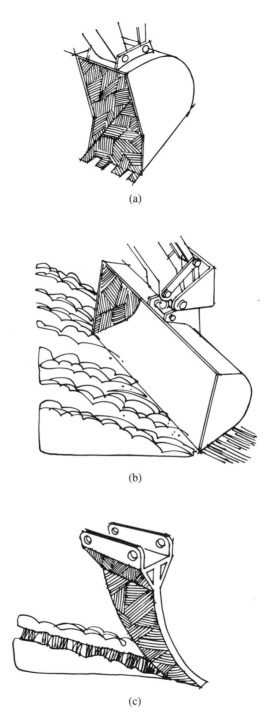

(a)

(b)

(c)

Figure 6–19. (a) Standard dipper. (b) Cleanout dipper. (c) Ripper. Source: Caterpillar.

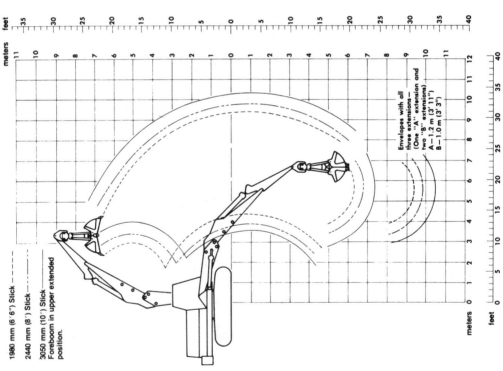

Maximum digging depth with two-piece boom with foreboom in upper, extended position and three extensions:

	m	ft
1980 mm (6'6") stick	9.4	30'9"
2440 mm (8') stick	9.8	32'3"
3050 mm (10') stick	10.4	34'3"
*With foreboom in lower, extended position, add	1.07	3'6"

*The one-piece boom has approximately the same working envelope as the two-piece boom with the foreboom in the lower, extended position.

1980 mm (6'6") Stick -------
2440 mm (8') Stick ----
3050 mm (10') Stick ———
Foreboom in upper extended position.

Envelopes with all three extensions—
(One "A" extension and two "B" extensions)
A—1.2 m (3'11")
B—1.0 m (3'3")

Figure 6–19. (Continued). (d) Clamshell attachment on Caterpillar 225 excavator. Note working ranges. Source: Caterpillar.

(d)

84

lift crane. But the machine can also be equipped with a dipper and used much like a backhoe: the telescoping boom is extended, the dipper is lowered, and the material is pulled back toward the machine. A revolving superstructure allows the boom to swing to the desired dump point, where the load is released. In addition to tilting up and down, the boom may also twist or rotate somewhat.

When equipped with a dipper, the telescoping boom is good for working long, straight grades such as drainage ditches or similar projects. When equipped with a hook, it is an excellent, very mobile lift crane (because of the rubber-tired carrier). Other attachments are also available. (See Figure 6–20.)

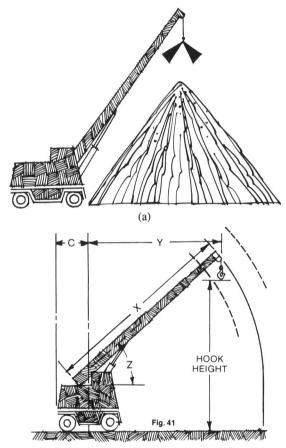

(a)

HOOK
HEIGHT

Fig. 41

C SWING CLEARANCE (RADIUS OF REAR END FROM
    AXIS OF ROTATION)
X BOOM LENGTH PIN-TO-PIN
Y RADIUS OF LOAD
Z BOOM ANGLE

Source: Power Crane and Shovel Association

(b)

Figure 6–20. The telescoping boom excavator and lift crane, with (a) clamshell and (b) hook.

PILEDRIVER

The major components of the typical piledriver include the crane boom (usually a lattice type), hoist drum laggings, cables, and pile driving equipment. Piledrivers drive several different kinds of wood, steel, and concrete piling for foundations, piers, wharves, bridge bents, and similar work. Several means of driving the piles are common, including the drop hammer, air, steam, and diesel power. (See Figure 6–21.)

When the drop hammer is used, the hammer slides up and down in guides called *pile driver leads*, which are suspended from the boom tip. The hammer is lifted by the hoist cable and then dropped down to strike the pile (thus the name, *hammer*). The pile, protected by a pile cap, is driven down by the blows.

Figure 6–21. Drophammer-type piledriver.

When air, steam, or diesel power is used, the hoist line holds the power hammer in position at the top of the piling, and the hammer drives the piling down.

The following operational techniques for the crane family of excavating equipment are suggested by the Power Crane and Shovel Association (PCSA):

1. Where repetitive lifting is involved, the crane should be positioned for the shortest possible swing cycle.

2. Crane footing should be checked carefully before lifting capacity or near-capacity loads. Ratings are based on firm, level footings.

3. All overhead obstructions should be inspected carefully before moving a crane or starting lifting operations. Position the machine to avoid any contact with power lines.

4. Rigging must be secure when attaching loads, and the lift started only when all helpers are in the clear.

5. The operator should swing the crane slowly enough to avoid excessive outward throw of the load and overswinging when the machine stops. Crane work is most controllable in slow motion. Fast swinging of crane loads can be dangerous and generally will lose more time than it gains, through loss of control.

6. Loads should be placed on solid footings so that they have no tendency to overbalance when released.

7. In figuring the height of a lift, the block, hook, and any slack in the sling between hook and load must be included. When making capacity lifts, the entire lifting cycle should be calculated and planned before picking up load. It takes less time and is much safer to check clearances and position than to lift and try, and then reposition and try again. With repetitive lifting, a planned cycle is the best way to high production at low costs.

8. Organize work for minimum travel time. All required lifts in the area should be completed before moving to another location.

9. Booming up and down lengthens the cycle and should be avoided as much as possible on repetitive lifting.

10. With rubber-mounted cranes, outriggers should be securely set before undertaking any near-capacity loads. Footing under jacks must be level and solid.

11. Jerky operations on crane work should be avoided. They are both hard on the machine and dangerous.

12. Adding a jib to the boom increases the working range both horizontally and vertically, but will reduce lifting capacity.

13. For a given boom length, the steeper the working angle, the shorter the working radius is. With each degree of boom movement to a more vertical position, there is a corresponding degree of reduction in boom radius—and a corresponding increase in lifting capacity.

14. In work involving a sequence of loads, the crane should be positioned to lift the loads to the most remote points first. This maneuver provides greater assurance of boom clearances and avoids blocking subsequent crane operations.

LOADERS

Loaders are also called tractor–shovels, scoop loaders, front-end loaders, and bucket loaders. In addition to loading and/or relocating loose materials such as earth, rock, concrete, asphalt, etc., they are sometimes used for excavation tasks similar to those performed at times by dozers. Wheeled loaders may be steered by the rear wheels. There are also articulated frame models available with a hinge point about midway between the front and rear axles which increases maneuverability. Both track and wheeled units exist. (See Figure 6–22.)

Two of the most used attachments are the scoop bucket and multisegment bucket. The scoop bucket does ordinary loading; the multisegment bucket may be used like the scoop bucket, or it may be opened up and used like a (power-operated) clamshell attachment. (See Figure 6–23.)

Many other attachments may be used with the loader, including forklifts, cleanup blades, dozer blades, rippers, snow blades, augers, cranes, and log grapples. A backhoe, attached to the rear of the machine, is frequently used in combination with the front-end attachment. Such an arrangement makes for a very versatile machine. (See Figure 6–24.) Wheeled, rubber-tired loaders can achieve speeds of over 25 miles per hour. The large rubber tires give them good traction, but not, of course, as good as that of crawler units. Crawler track units have better traction but lower speeds. As usual, job conditions determine whether tires or tracks are used.

In addition to the general uses mentioned previously, typical jobs for loaders include loading hoppers and skips; loading, unloading, and carrying construction supplies and materials such as concrete, concrete forms, pipes, generators, and pumps; towing trailers; basement and miscellaneous excavations; and cleanup work. Some suggested operating techniques are:

1. Begin loading material by allowing the bucket edge to just touch the ground surface. Then, moving at slow speed, let the material crowd into the bucket, lowering the bucket somewhat. As the material crowds in, roll the bucket back so that the material does not spill out.

Source: Caterpillar Tractor

(a)

Source: Caterpillar Tractor

(b)

Figure 6–22. Loaders are available in (a) track units and (b) wheeled units.

(a)

Source: John Deere   (b)

Figure 6–23. Two of the most used attachments include (a) the scoop bucket and (b) the multisegment bucket.

Source: John Deere   (a)

Source: John Deere   (b)

Figure 6–24. Many attachments are available for loaders.

(c)

Source: Clark

(d)

Figure 6–24. (Continued).

2. Plan the work route and the arrangement of load-receiving equipment such that the travel time and maneuvering time of the loader is minimized.

3. Use the appropriate attachment for the job. The multisegment bucket works better with sticky clays and similar materials than does the standard scoop bucket. Use the ripper on hard materials before attempting to load.

LIFTING CAPACITY

The lifting capacity of an excavator, or the load it can lift, is one of the primary considerations in the selection of an excavator. Excavators are frequently used to dig trenches, lift and swing heavy pipe into trenches, load and unload trucks, and lift and swing manholes into position. The materials and supplies used in these operations have different weights, and thus different lifting capacities are required to perform the work. Because of the great cost of construction equipment, the manager is interested in getting the machine that performs best for the work it will do. He or she does not want to pay for too much machine or buy a machine that will not do the job.

Essentially, lifting capacity depends on four factors:

1. The weight of the machine
2. The location of the machine's center of gravity
3. The length of radius from the machine swing centerline to the attachment
4. The power of the unit

The way in which these four factors influence lifting capacity is fairly obvious:

1. Every machine will reach a point where the load would be so heavy relative to the weight of the machine, that the machine would tip over toward the load.

2. Machines with a low center of gravity would be less likely to tip over than machines with a high center of gravity.

3. The machine can lift less weight when the attachment is fully extended than it can when the attachment is somewhat closer to the machine (just as you can hold less weight with your arms extended than with them held close to your chest).

4. The more power the machine has, the more weight it can lift.

Other factors besides those just listed affect lifting capacity—footing, for example. Firm footing should be provided for best lifting capacity, and sometimes for safety. Level footing is necessary for safety. Outriggers, counterweights, and other devices may be used to increase lifting capacity.

Maximum lifting capacity is achieved when the boom and load are in line with the longitudinal axis of the carrier or mounting. The condition of the machine is also important, as maximum lifting capacities apply only to new machines. As a machine ages, its maximum lifting capacity usually lessens from the manufacturer's ratings. This is important to realize if one is either considering buying a used machine or estimating production for used machines. (See Figure 6–25.)

Finally, the excavator has an optimum lifting range relative to the ground line. That is, loads deep down, such as those at the bottom of deep trenches, and high loads, such as those that have to be lifted up to a platform or the upper floors of a building, are more difficult to handle than loads that are at a closer distance to the ground line. (See Figure 6–26.)

How to read backhoe lift capacity

- Figures used indicate <u>rated</u> lift capacities, which are 87% of maximum lift force according to SAE J31 definition. <u>Maximum</u> lift capacity is 115% of rated capacity.
- Lift capacities are listed in small type on the right and left sides of the chart.
- Boom cylinder lift capacities are shown on the left, <u>dipperstick</u> capacities on the right. Capacities are given in pounds and kilograms at various points in the lifting cycle.
- Numbers above each line show capacities for "over end" lifting, when the boom is within a 45-degree swing from the tractor center line. Numbers below the line show "swing arc" capacities, with the boom 90 degrees right or left of center.
- Numbers in large type on the right side of the chart indicate height in feet at which capacities were calculated. The "O" indicates ground (or other supporting surface) level.
- Numbers in large type running horizontally across the chart indicate distance in feet from the swing pivot center line.
- The long heavy curved line indicates the boom lift arc. The short heavy curved line indicates the dipperstick lift arc. The straight heavy lines represent the boom and dipperstick.
- Example: For the 15-ft backhoe, the <u>rated</u> lift capacity of the dipperstick is 3,900 pounds at 6-ft height, about 9-ft from the swing post.

LIFT CAPACITY (per SAE J31)

Lift capacities shown are 87% of maximum lift force, according to SAE definition.

Series 765 15-ft backhoe.

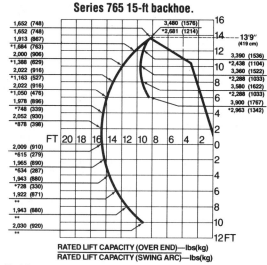

RATED LIFT CAPACITY (OVER END)—lbs(kg)
RATED LIFT CAPACITY (SWING ARC)—lbs(kg)

*Stability limited. Others hydraulically limited. **Not available.

Source: Ford Tractor Operations

Figure 6–25. Lifting capacity chart for Ford 765 15-ft backhoe. Note the outriggers (front view of machine).

DIMENSIONS (per SAE J49)

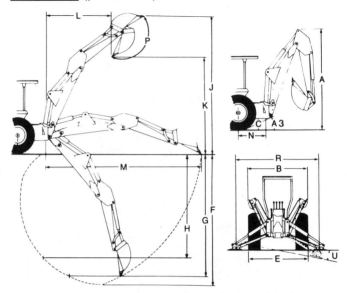

		15-ft backhoe ft, in. (cm)	15-ft backhoe with ext. dipperstick ft, in. (cm)
A	Transport height	12′ (365.8)	11′10″ (360.7)
B	Stabilizer spread transport	7′1″ (215.9)	7′1″ (215.9)
C	Ground clearance	1′ (30.4)	1′ (30.4)
	Overall length	23′ (701)	23′ (701)
E	Overall width	7′1″ (215.9)	7′1″ (215.9)
F	Digging depth, maximum	15′5″ (469.9)	19′4″ (589.3)
G	Digging depth, 2 ft flat bottom	15′3″ (464.8)	19′2″ (584.2)
H	Digging depth, 8 ft flat bottom	14′1″ (429.3)	18′3″ (556.2)
J	Overall operating height, fully raised	16′4″ (497.8)	17′11″ (546.1)
K	Loading height	11′5″ (348)	12′9″ (401.3)
L	Loading reach	7′9″ (236.2)	11′7″ (353.1)
M	Reach from swing pivot	19′3″ (586.8)	22′11″ (698.5)
N	Swing pivot to rear wheels	3′6.5″ (108)	3′6.5″ (108)
P	Bucket rotation	153/179 degrees	153/179 degrees
	Swing arc	180 degrees	180 degrees
R	Stabilizer spread operating	10′ (304.8)	10′ (304.8)
U	Leveling angle	11 degrees	11 degrees
A3	Angle of departure (per SAE J1234)	16 degrees	16 degrees

Working Weight (approx.)

With 15-ft backhoe, cab, counterweights, and general material loader bucket	13,750 lbs (6237 kg)
With 15-ft backhoe and extendible dipperstick, cab, counterweights, and general material loader bucket	14,698 lbs (6667 kg)

Optional backhoe counterweight group: front end weight plus two lower side and two upper side weights. Total weight: 830 lbs (376.5 kg). Not required and cannot be installed when loader is equipped with multi-purpose bucket.

Figure 6–25. (Continued).

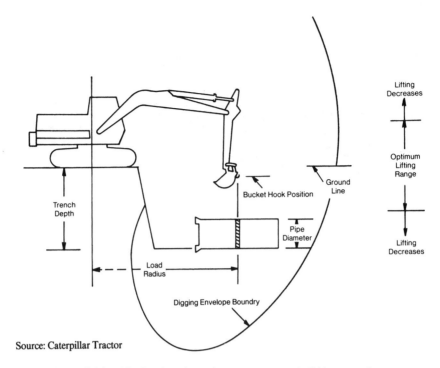

Lifting
Decreases

Optimum
Lifting
Range

Lifting
Decreases

Ground
Line

Bucket Hook Position

Pipe
Diameter

Trench
Depth

Load
Radius

Digging Envelope Boundry

Figure 6–26. This drawing shows how an excavator's lifting capacity can vary with load position.

HAULING EQUIPMENT

7

DUMP TRUCKS

Dump trucks are the most frequently used equipment for hauling materials over considerable distances. Specific job conditions determine the best hauling method, but dump trucks are not usually used for distances less than 1,500 feet.

There are many sizes and types of dump trucks. The body size and configuration are largely determined by the type of material to be hauled and the terrain over which it will be transported. Sand, for example, can be dumped and spread easily from almost any truck. Clays and other sticky materials tend to adhere to sharp corners and angular body shapes, and thus rounded corners are desirable for these materials. Very broadly, dump trucks may be said to be *general-purpose* vehicles, used to haul earth, gravel, sand, relatively small rock or ore, and mixed materials. There are, however, some *special-purpose* dump trucks, used to haul large rocks and boulders, or other materials requiring a special configuration, strength, power, etc.

Dump trucks are available with gasoline or diesel engines with a wide range of power options. They also may have two-wheel or four-wheel drive, and two or three axles. The general-purpose dump truck is usually suitable for highway use. Off-highway trucks are much larger vehicles capable of hauling over 100 tons of material. Authorities limit the amount of weight and the size of vehicles that may be placed on public highways. (See Figure 7–1.)

Capacities. The capacity of a dump truck (or similar hauling equipment) may be expressed in at least three ways:

1. The rated capacity, expressed in tons
2. The struck volume, expressed in cubic yards
3. The heaped capacity, expressed in cubic yards

The weight capacity should not be exceeded, as doing so contributes to excessive wear on the machine and usually would not be productive anyway because of reduced hauling speed and/or spilling. The maximum load that can be hauled, in practice, is limited by volume when light loads are carried and by weight when heavy loads are carried. Dry clays may weigh as little as 1,700 pounds per cubic yard, while concrete may weigh almost 4,000 pounds per cubic yard.

For the most efficient hauling operation, the size and number of trucks should be balanced with the workload of the excavators. That is, in a smoothly run haul cycle, the size and number of trucks should be planned so that the excavator(s) and trucks are kept as uniformly busy as practicable. Trucks should not be lined up waiting to be loaded (although having one or more vehicles in reserve is a frequent and reasonable practice). (See Figure 7–2.)

Figure 7–1. Wabco off-highway dump truck. This machine will carry approximately 150 tons of material.

Figure 7–2. The size and number of trucks should be balanced with the workload of the excavators so that all machines are kept as uniformly busy as practicable.

WAGONS

Wagons are similar in appearance to tractor–scrapers but are neither self-loading nor self-propelled; they are for carrying only. A given wagon usually may be hauled by a variety of tractors, but the tractor should be appropriately matched to the size of the wagon. Specially designed tractor–wagons are also available.

Wagons come in end-dump, side-dump, and bottom-dump models. Flow gates are available which aid in spreading the material as it is dumped from the wagon bottom. These gates spread material longitudinally or crosswise (called cross flow), and some gates will spread material either way. Cross flow gates aid in spreading aggregates, base materials, and the like. Longitudinal flow gates are used for windrowing, stockpiling, and similar operations. (See Figure 7–3.)

Several suggested hauling techniques are:

Figure 7–3. Wabco bottom dump wagon. This wagon is being used in a coal operation.

1. Excavators are normally the prime factors in determining the number of trucks or wagons. Accordingly, utilize the most efficient excavation methods and use enough trucks or haul units so that the excavators are always busy.

2. Avoid waiting lines for trucks beyond one or two (more if conditions demand) in reserve. Reserve trucks may be kept busy on work near excavators and brought into the haul cycle should haul truck break down or should the need for additional haul trucks otherwise become apparent (e.g., if the excavator is not working to maximum capability).

3. Fill trucks to the maximum capacity practicable, depending on their capability, the condition of haul roads, the severity of road grades, etc. Never overload trucks, as breakdown time and costs exceed any benefits possible due to overloading.

4. Use the appropriate truck body for haul material, and keep the truck clean. Oil or otherwise lubricate dump bodies before hauling bituminous materials. Spray bodies with water before hauling concrete, and do not allow concrete to set on bodies.

5. In mixed loads, load the heaviest materials toward the rear of the truck to ease the burden on hydraulic equipment.

6. Use spotting blocks or logs to aid truck operators in getting in position to receive their loads.

7. Operate trucks at the highest possible safe speeds. Do not speed.

8. Study traffic patterns and minimize backing up, turnarounds, passing, etc., accordingly. Where practicable, use separate roads to and from the dump area.

9. Where spreading is being done at the dump area, keep trucks moving as they dump, in order to aid dozers and/or graders.

10. Do not allow trucks to bunch up at the dump area. Establish additional dump sites if necessary.

EQUIPMENT TRAILERS

Equipment trailers are used to transport construction equipment over long distances (distances beyond their efficient operating ranges, from site to site, etc.). Crane–shovels, crawler–tractors, and similar equipment are typical loads for equipment trailers. Supplies like lumber, pipe, reinforcing steel, precast concrete panels, brick, concrete structural members, and steel members are also often transported by equipment trailers. (See Figure 7–4.)

(a)

(b)

Figure 7–4. Equipment trailers manufactured by the Talbert Company. (a) Note the modular design. (b) Typical uses include equipment and supply hauling.

A wide range of power, load capacities, drive, and body configurations is available. The following are commonly used operating techniques for equipment trailers:

1. Use docks, earth ramps, etc., to load and unload equipment where practicable. A trailer should always carry its own ramps in case the foregoing cannot be used.

2. Secure equipment to the trailer with chains or other suitable devices, and block equipment carefully at the trailer bed.

3. Balance equipment properly on the trailer.

4. Load and unload slowly and carefully. Provide a worker to direct the equipment operator in loading and unloading equipment.

FORKLIFTS

Forklifts are normally associated with warehouse loading, e.g., for lifting and placing palletized loads and boxes. (See Figure 7–5.) However, they are also frequently used in construction operations for loading and unloading trucks, trailers, flat cars, and the like.

Source: John Deere

Figure 7–5. Fork lifts are most commonly used for warehouse loading. However, special attachments are available for use in rough terrain, snow, mud, water, etc., so that the forklift may be used out of doors. High lift attachments also are available.

Although most forklifts used in construction operations are designed and used only as forklifts per se, special forklift attachments are available for various loaders that make them suitable for use in rough terrain, water, snow, mud, etc. Also, forklift attachments are sometimes combined with hydraulic cranes for high lift capabilities.

Some suggested forklift operating techniques are:

1. Do not exceed load capacity.

2. Position the forklift head-on to the load if practicable.

3. Maintain proper tire pressure. Lower pressures are usually used for rough, slippery, or muddy terrain, higher pressures for smooth surfaces.

4. When transporting, keep loads low and close to the frame of the forklift.

8

DRILLING, BLASTING, AND PROCESSING EQUIPMENT

PIT AND QUARRY OPERATIONS

Stone aggregate is a frequent requirement on construction projects. It is obtained from *pits* and *quarries,* which are sites where these mineral aggregates are found in quantity.

Both pits and quarries are open excavations. For the purposes of this text, the main difference between them is that aggregate is usually loosened from quarries using *drilling and blasting* equipment, whereas aggregate may be extracted from pits using the equipment previously discussed—power shovels, draglines, etc. Table 8–1 presents some differences and similarities of pit and quarry operations, equipment use, etc.

LOCATING THE QUARRY SITE

Care must be taken in selecting the quarry site because large rock processing facilities often are difficult to move. Crushing, screening, and other rock processing equipment should be located as near to the quarry as possible. And, of course, the site must be capable of yielding the volume and type of rock needed. Typically, the processing equipment is placed as close to the quarry as possible, within the limits of safety governed by the blasting operations in the quarry. Obviously, it is advantageous to minimize the hauling distance between the quarry and the processing equipment. In ideal circumstances, the processing equipment is placed within efficient operating ranges of dozers or similar equipment, and the trucks and haul units may then be used exclusively to transport finished crushed stone aggregate (aggregate crushed to meet size requirements) to the project site, thereby eliminating quarry hauls, which usually contain clay and other by-products that the processing plant removes.

Terrain is important in quarry selection, as the efficient operation of haul units and other construction equipment is greatly affected by grades, drainage, and the like. Thus, the site should drain well and be without adverse grades. Also, sites with a minimum of earthwork to do are desirable.

There should be enough space to provide ample mobility for the moving equipment, accommodate the processing equipment, and allow for storage and future expansion.

Sites that utilize existing public utilities are advantageous. Otherwise, water and power needs must be arranged for by the contractor. A rough rule of thumb for water requirements is that the number of tons of aggregate produced per hour multiplied by 10 should be equal to the number of gallons of water per minute required.

Table 8–1. Classification of pits and quarries. Pits and quarries are both open excavations. Pits typically contain material that can be removed with ordinary excavation equipment. Quarries usually contain more consolidated material that must first be loosened by drilling and blasting operations before it is excavated.

TYPE	MATERIAL	PRIMARY USE	WATER CONDITION	OPERATIONS AND EQUIPMENT
PIT:				
Borrow	Select soil other than gravel and sand.	Embankment and subgrades.	Dry	Earth-moving equipment, dozer, power shovel, rooter or dragline.
Gravel:				
(Bank-hill)	Gravel and sand with clay.	Base courses, surfacing, and fills.	Dry	Power shovel, loader or hand.
(Alluvial)	Clean gravel and sand.	Aggregate for concrete and bituminous mixes.	Wet (or dry).	Dragline, power shovel, or hand.
Miscellaneous (dumps).	Mine spoil, slag, cinders, etc.	Surfacing and aggregates.	Dry	Power shovel, loader or hand.
QUARRY:				
Hard rock[1]	Aggregate	Base courses, surfacing and aggregate for concrete and bituminous mixes.	Dry	Drilling, blasting, crushing, screening. Drilling tools, crushing, screening (and washing) plant.
Medum rock[2]	Aggregate	Base courses, surfacing.	....	Drilling, blasting, crushing, screening, washing. Drilling tools, shovel and crushing, screening (and washing) plant.
Soft rock[3]	Cementaceous material.	Base courses and surfacing on roads and airfields.	Dry	Rooter, power shovel, earth-moving equipment.

[1]Hard rock—granite, trap, schist, gneiss, and so on.
[2]Medium rock—some limestone, some sandstone, and so on.
[3]Soft rock—soft coral, tuff, caliche, chalk, some limestone, some sandstone, and so on.

Source: U. S. Department of the Army.

Water is used to wash away by-products (e.g., clay) from the aggregate, to wash the equipment, and for other purposes. If there is excess water, it is often routed to on-site detention ponds or "settling basins" to avoid contamination of streams, lakes, and land, and to avoid excessive use of public storm drain lines. Water may be siphoned off the settling basins and reused to wash raw aggregate. If power is brought to the site, the power units should be carefully selected to match the needs of the processing equipment. Typically, crushing equipment requires 60-cycle power.

DRILLING EQUIPMENT

To loosen hard rock, holes are drilled in a planned pattern, explosive charges are set, and the rock is then blasted loose. Excavating equipment may then be used to load haul units and/or move the raw aggregate to the processing plant.

Compressors. Drilling equipment is typically powered by compressed air. Compressors may be mounted on various-sized trailers, trucks, etc., as needed. Many power sizes are available, from 100 cubic feet per minute to over 1,000 cubic feet per minute. (See Figure 8–1.)

Drill Steel. Drill steel is used with pneumatic tools. The diameters and lengths vary with the type of equipment and power; generally, from about 1 to 5½ inches in diameter and 2 to 24 feet in length are available. The drills have a hollow center to allow dust and chips to be forced out. Air is often used for this purpose, as is water. (Water keeps the drill cooler, which is sometimes required.) (See Figure 8–2.)

Jackhammer. The jackhammer, or portable pneumatic drill, is a compressed air-powered, percussion-type drill that can be operated by one person when operated vertically. The machine weighs about 50 pounds. Jackhammers can drill over 20 foot deep where practicable, but 10-foot depths are more typical. Hole diameters are usually from about 1 to 2 inches. In addition to drilling, jackhammers are frequently fitted with blades or similar tools to break up concrete, asphalt, etc.

Typically, jackhammers deliver over 2,000 blows per minute. Air or water is used through the drill to force the dust and chips out and keep the steel cool. (See Figure 8–3.)

Drifters. Drifters look and work like large jackhammers. They are usually mounted on hydraulic booms and thus can drill down, up, horizontally, and at an angle. These drills find much use in quarries, and they are almost always found in tunnel and mining operations. Hole sizes range from about 2½ to 5½ inches in diameter for depths of about 12 feet, depending on drifter model, power, etc.

Track-mounted Drills. Track-mounted drills combine a hydraulic boom and mast mounted on tracks. Thus, they can travel in almost any terrain. Hole diameters range up to about 6 inches, with depths of over 50 feet. (See Figure 8–4.)

Source: Ingersoll-Rand   (a)

Source: LeRoi   (b)

Figure 8–1. (a) Portable air compressor. (b) Stationary air compressor.

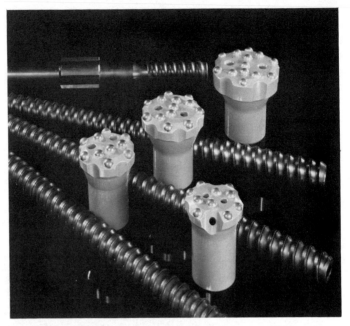

Source: Ingersoll-Rand (a)

Source: LeRoi (b)

Figure 8–2. (a) Drill steel and bits. (b) Drills are usually used for 1- to 5½-inch diameter holes. This one, however, drills a 30-inch diameter hole in rock.

Source: Ingersoll-Rand

Figure 8–3. Jackhammer. This one is fitted with a blade, not a drill. Note the portable air compressor.

Truck-mounted drills. Where terrain permits, and where high mobility is desired, various-sized truck drills are available. With such equipment, vertical and angle drilling are possible. Hole diameters are over 6 inches and depth is over 50 feet. (See Figure 8–5.)

Other Drills. The drills just discussed are commonly used in quarry work. Still other drills and configurations are available for various special conditions and uses.

Selecting Drilling Equipment

Three essential factors that influence drill selection are:

1. *Terrain.* Which drill can move or be moved around the site conveniently?

(a)

(b)

Figure 8–4. Track-mounted drills being used in highway work.

Source: Ingersoll-Rand

Figure 8–5. Truck-mounted drill.

2. *Size of holes*. Small, relatively shallow holes may be done with jackhammers. Large holes may require drifters or other, heavier duty equipment.
3. *Number of holes*. The speeds of the different kinds of drilling equipment vary widely. Select the equipment that can do the job within the time constraints of the schedule.

BLASTING EQUIPMENT

Generally speaking, the purpose of blasting is to separate areas of hard rock from the rest of the site, such that the rock may then be extracted and processed efficiently. This separation is accomplished by drilling *blastholes* in strategic patterns, loading them with explosives, and then detonating them.

Explosives. Some explosives have great heaving power and a low rate of detonation, a combination that is preferred for blasting materials such as soft rock. Conversely, a high rate of detonation is preferable for blasting hard rock.

Thus, the different detonating characteristics of explosives are exploited to produce desired movement in quarry materials. Table 8–2 lists some common explosives, together with their characteristics and uses.

Electric Blasting Caps. Electric blasting caps are used to start detonation in high explosives. The blasting caps are positioned within electrical circuits, and a time delay is used to create the desired firing sequence.

Primacord. Primacord is a type of nonelectric fuse used to detonate high explosives. The fuse consists of a small core of high-explosive material sheathed to achieve a degree of rigidity, strength, and water resistance. One or more primacord fuses, if used in place of electric blasting caps, are run the full depth of the blast hole. Primacord fuses themselves are usually detonated with an electric blasting cap located at an appropriate end of the fuse or fuses.

Safety

There are many potential hazards involved in the transportation, handling, use, and storage of explosives. Thus, specialists are often contracted to handle many of the tasks associated with explosives.

Federal, state, and local laws govern the transportation of explosive materials to the site. Once the explosives reach the site, there is the problem of safe storage. Accordingly, the excavator or the other contractors typically request delivery from the explosive supplier on an as-needed basis. However, even with such minimization of the amount of explosive on site, there remains the problem of the storage facility, or magazine, itself. Typically, magazines are bullet and fire resistant, weatherproof, and well ventilated. On-site transportation of explosives from the storage facility to the bore holes must be carefully planned and executed.

The following safety precautions are not exhaustive but should give the reader an idea of what is involved in the handling and use of explosives:

1. Keep detonators and explosives a safe distance apart until they are ready for hookup.
2. Protect all explosives from friction, sparks, fire, and shock.
3. Keep explosives dry.
4. Keep the site clean of explosive containers, container covers, etc., and dispose of such items properly.
5. Do not allow untrained workers to handle or use explosives.
6. Do not work in the storage facility. That is, do not open explosive containers, rig explosives, etc. Similarly, do not store other materials or tools in the storage facility.
7. Keep construction equipment and workers away from the area where blastholes are being loaded.

Table 8–2. *Characteristics of explosives. Different explosives have different detonation rates. These differences are exploited to produce the desired movement in quarry materials.*

NAME	PRINCIPAL USE	SMALLEST CAP REQUIRED FOR DETONATION	VELOCITY OF DETONATION (FT. PER SEC)	RELATIVE EFFECTIVENESS AS EXTERNAL CHARGE	INTENSITY OF POISONOUS FUMES	WATER RESISTANCE
Military dynamite	Quarry and rock cuts	Special military cap, electric or nonelectric.	20,000	1.00	Dangerous	Good
Straight dynamite 40% 50% (commercial) 60%		....	15,000 18,000 19,000	.71 .86 .90	Dangerous	Good (if fired within 24 hr.)
Ammonia dynamite 40% 50% (commercial) 60%	Land clearings, cratering, quarrying, and general use in rear areas.	No. 6 commercial cap, electric or nonelectric.	9,000 11,000 12,000	.45 .50 .58	Dangerous	Poor
Gelatin dynamite 40% 50% 60%			8,000 9,000 16,000	.46 .51 .83	Slight	Good

Source: U. S. Department of the Army.

117

8. Keep construction equipment and workers away from the explosion site until the demolition supervisor decides otherwise.

9. Keep workers and equipment a safe distance away from blasts.

In summary, blasting requires knowledge, skill, and experience; mistakes can be very unforgiving. Obviously, the foregoing text is very general: the scope of this text does not permit a full treatment of blasting equipment, procedures, and safety rules. For a full treatment of explosives and blasting procedures, interested readers should consult standard textbooks on the subject plus manufacturers' literature.

AGGREGATE PROCESSING EQUIPMENT

As mentioned at the beginning of this chapter, stone aggregate is much used in construction projects. Aggregate is obtained from pit and quarry sites. Pits are primarily sites from which gravel and sand are extracted using typical earthmoving equipment. Little or no blasting is required in typical pit operations. Quarries, on the other hand, are sources of stone that must be blasted loose. After the raw stone is blasted loose, it must then be processed into the various stone aggregate sizes suitable for use as paving bases, in concrete and asphalt, etc.

Processing plants for producing crushed stone aggregate vary in size and sophistication. (See Figure 8–6.) But regardless of the seeming complexity of the operation, there are only four tasks involved:

1. Reducing the size of raw stone by *crushing*.
2. Separating the crushed aggregate into standard particle sizes by *screening*.
3. *Transporting* material from one component to another and to stockpiles, etc.
4. Eliminating by-products (such as clay) by *washing*.

Before proceeding with a discussion of the major components of stone aggregate processing equipment, the following terms should be briefly reviewed.

Blocking. Blocking means the blockading of the crusher receiving opening by a piece of stone that is too large to enter the crushing chamber in any position.

Bridging. Bridging means the blockading within the receiving opening by one or more pieces, any of which are small enough to enter the crushing

Figure 8–6. Regardless of the complex appearance of aggregate processing plants, there are only four operations: crushing, screening, transporting, and washing.

chamber, but which are prevented from doing so, because they either fall so as to span the opening or mutually block each other from entrance.

Choke-feeding. Choke-feeding means the feeding of a completely filled crushing chamber (or one as full as the design will permit), with a sufficient head of material above the receiving opening to keep the crusher full continuously. This contrasts with regulated feeding, which implies that the flow of material to the crusher is throttled to a point somewhat below the capacity of the machine, so that the crusher is never completely filled.

Choking. Choking means a complete, or practically complete, stoppage of the downward flow of material in the crushing chamber. It may be the result of an external condition, such as a backup of material caused by an obstruction in the discharge chute, in which case choking is followed by packing in the crusher chamber. Or it may be the result of a condition existing within the crusher chamber, such as too close a discharge setting, too many fines in the feed, or sticky material. When so caused, packing precedes—and brings about—the choke-up.

Choke-point. The choke-point in a crushing chamber is that level in the chamber where its cross-sectional area is smallest. It is the point where choking is most likely to occur, particularly so if the choke is promoted by a condition existing within the crusher.

Closed Side. A closed side is that discharge opening that exists when a jaw or gyratory crusher is at its minimum during any one cycle.

Degradation. Degradation is the breakage of material caused by handling or weathering.

Desliming. Desliming is the washing of micron-size particles from a product by passing it over a screen and subjecting it to water sprays.

Dewatering. Dewatering is the removal of surface moisture. It may be partially accomplished by screening to remove undersize material.

Grizzly. A grizzly is a screening surface composed of parallel bars. The bars are usually tapered toward the discharge end to prevent clogging. Grizzlies are intended for coarse scalping and may be either fixed, movable, or vibrating.

Mesh. Mesh is the number of openings per lineal inch of wire cloth or screen.

Oversize. Oversize is the material that stays on a given screen.

Open Side. An open side is that discharge opening that exists when a jaw or gyratory crusher is at its maximum during any one cycle.

Packing. *a*. Packing refers to a compacted or compressed condition of the material in the crusher, characterized by a complete or nearly complete absence of voids. Any condition which tends to retard the free movement of material downward through the crushing chamber tends likewise to promote packing. *b*. Packing is also used to describe the building up of fine, sticky material on the diaphragm of a gyratory crusher, or in the discharge chute below any type of crusher.

Percentage of Open Area. The percentage of open area is the ratio of the combined area of the openings to the total area of screening surface.

Primary Crusher. A primary crusher is the first crusher in a plant designed to handle the material from a quarry or gravel deposit.

Rescreen. Rescreen is a screen used to remove degradation or undersize from a product not removed by prior screening operations.

Revolving Screens. Revolving screens are cylinders mounted on rollers, with the screen surface around the circumference.

Road Metal. Road metal is crushed rock, gravel, slag, and similar materials which are used in surface or base-course construction and maintenance.

Rod Deck. Rod deck is a screen surface composed of parallel round rods for scalping similar to a grizzly.

Run of Mine. Run of mine is the material as it comes from the quarry or mine without being treated in any way.

Scalping. Scalping is removing coarse oversize material, usually ahead of a crusher.

Scrubber Screen. A scrubber screen is a revolving cylindrical screen that is normally employed inside a drum, with a scrubbing section of blank plate containing lifters to agitate the material and cast it upon the screen for further sizing.

Secondary Crusher. A secondary crusher is a crusher that further reduces the product of another crusher.

Shaking Screens. Shaking screens are long screen bodies hung from flexible supports and driven by eccentrics. They have a long stroke at relatively low speed.

Size Consist. Size consist is the fractional size breakdown of a material as determined by a sieve analysis. It may be expressed as the percent of the whole between two sieve sizes or by cumulative percentages.

Sizing. Sizing is the process of dividing a mixture of grains of different sizes into groups or grades whose characteristic is that the particles therein are more or less nearly of the same size, all having passed an aperture of certain dimensions and failed to pass through some smaller aperture.

Stage of Reduction. The stage of reduction of a material is the difference in maximum input and maximum output size of the material due to a single crushing action. Stage of reduction can be expressed in inches or centimeters. A stage of reduction of 3 inches (7.6 centimeters) would indicate a 3-inch (7.6-centimeter) reduction in maximum particle size.

Tramp Iron. Tramp iron is any metal that finds its way into the crushing chamber.

Trommel Screens. Trommel screens are similar to revolving screens, except that they are carried on a through shaft instead of rollers.

Undersize. Undersize is the material that passes through a given screen.

Washing. Washing is the use of water sprays over a screen deck to remove clay and other foreign substances.

Overburden. Overburden is the soil mantle, clay, sand, and gravel or low-grade rock lying above the rock to be quarried and beneath the ground surface.

Clay and Silt. The unconsolidated material, finer than 200 mesh (.074 millimeter), resulting from the natural disintegration of rocks.

Sand. The unconsolidated granular material coarser than 200 mesh (.074 millimeter) and finer than ¼ inch (6.35 millimeters), resulting from the natural disintegration of rocks.

Gravel. The unconsolidated material coarser than ¼ inch (6.35 millimeters) and finer than 3½ inches (88.9 millimeters).

Pebbles. Identical with gravel.

Cobbles. The same as pebbles, except larger than 3½ inches (88.9 millimeters) and less than 10 inches (25.4 centimeters) in size.

Boulders. The same as cobbles, except larger than 10 inches (25.4 centimeters) in size.

Fine Aggregate. Sand or finely crushed stone passing through a ¼-inch (6.35-millimeter) screen.

Coarse Aggregate. Natural or crushed gravel or crushed stone retained on a ¼-inch (6.35-millimeter) screen and passing through a 6-inch (15.2-centimeter) screen.

Binder. Any material which, because of its physical characteristics, is suitable for binding road metal into a coherent mass to withstand traffic impact with a minimum of displacement. Examples of binders are fine limestone, aggregate, moil, clay, silt, bituminous materials, cement, and saline solutions.

ROCK CRUSHERS

Rock crushers receive the raw material that has been broken loose by drilling and blasting operations. Their function is to reduce the relatively large pieces of rock (too large for most construction uses) to smaller sizes. There is no hard-and-fast classification of rock crushers, but generally, they may be categorized according to the stage or degree of crushing they do: *primary* rock crushers handle the largest stones that can be processed; *secondary* crushers receive the stones from the primary crushers and reduce their size further; and, finally, *tertiary* crushers, in turn, receive the stones from the secondary crushers and reduce their size again.

Several varieties of each of these rock crushers are available, and specific job conditions and product requirements determine the number and type of crushers needed. (See Figures 8–7 and 8–8.)

Prescreening. Prescreening raw material before it is loaded into the mechanical feeder often increases efficiency. One of the common prescreening devices is called a *grizzly*. A simple grizzly may be field constructed by building a screen (with appropriate size openings) of heavy steel bars, rails, etc. When the raw material is loaded onto the grizzly, all stones that are either too large for the crusher or adequate to be used without further crushing are separated. By-products are also separated out of the mass. Thus, prescreening in-

(a)

(b)

Figure 8–7. (a) Eccentric jaw rock crusher. These machines are used for primary reduction of quarry and mining materials. (b) Note the loading hopper. Machines manufactured by Barber-Greene.

Figure 8–8. Gyrashere rock crusher. The machine shown, by Barber Greene Co., is available in two sizes—one for coarse and intermediate material, and one for fine material.

creases crusher production and efficiency by reducing unnecessary loads on the crusher. Besides the simple grizzly, more sophisticated commercial models are available. (See Figure 8–9.)

SCREENS

Screens made of open mesh wire are used to separate the crushed stone from the rock crushers into a variety of standard sizes. Perhaps the most typical arrangement is two to four layers of screen mounted in a rectangular-shaped box. A vibrating device is attached to the screen box so that the aggregate fed into the box is separated into different sizes determined by the screen openings. Other screen configurations are used, but the function remains the same: to separate crushed rock particles into the desired range of standard sizes for construction use. (See Figure 8–10.)

Figure 8–9. Vibrating grizzly. This machine sifts out the fines, so that only oversize material is delivered to the primary crusher.

Figure 8–10. Vibrating screen. This screen, available in various sizes, can be used for rinsing, sizing, dewatering, and scalping, in addition to sizing.

MECHANICAL FEEDERS AND CONVEYORS

Mechanical feeders and conveyors are *transporting* and *regulating* components. All processing components work best if there is a uniform, optimum amount of materials available. Rock crushers, for example, can be overwhelmed by too large loads of raw stone. Conversely, if they are not adequately loaded, they are not operating efficiently. Mechanical feeders accept the initial loads of stone and then regulate the flow to the crushers.

Belt conveyors are commonly used to transport aggregate from component to component, to stockpiles, and to trucks or other points. The inclines of the conveyors are adjusted for job conditions and materials. Typical angles are from about 12 degrees for washed gravel up to as much as 20 degrees for loose earth. (See Figures 8–11 and 8–12.)

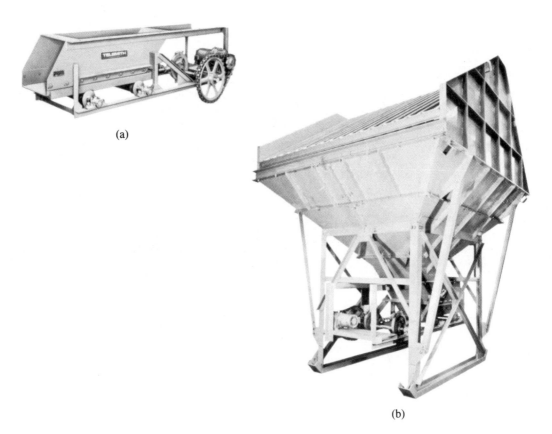

(a)

(b)

Figure 8–11. (a) Standard Plate feeder. (b) Plate feeder with hopper and bar grizzly.

Figure 8–12. Belt conveyor. Used to transport material from component to component, to trucks to stockpiles, etc.

WASHING EQUIPMENT

Crushed stone aggregate for construction use should be free of dirt, organic matter, and other ''impurities.'' Accordingly, various equipment is available for washing aggregate. The exact equipment used depends largely on the type of material to be removed and the particle sizes being cleaned. For example, removing clay from large stones requires different equipment from that used to clean small aggregate or sand. (See Figure 8–13.)

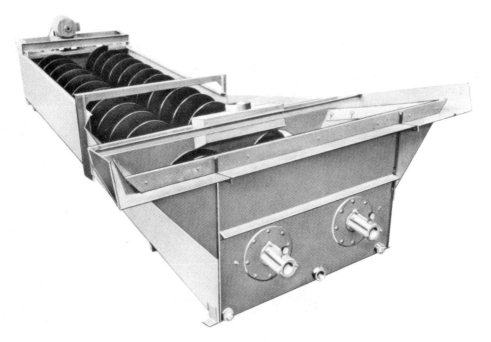

Figure 8–13. Double-screw washer. This machine also sizes and dewaters materials.

9

ASPHALT AND CONCRETE PLANTS AND EQUIPMENT

ASPHALT PLANTS

Bituminous surfaces are used throughout the world for highways, roads, streets, parking areas, airfields, and similar wearing surfaces. These surfaces consist of a variety of aggregate sizes held together by a *binder*. Typical aggregates include crushed stone, gravel, and sand. Other aggregates such as slag are sometimes used. Aggregates make up just over 90% of the weight of bituminous mix.

Aggregates give the bituminous surface its strength. The different sizes of aggregate reduce the number of voids, while the function of the binder is to coat and hold the aggregates together, providing a tough, waterproof surface. The binder is a bituminous material, mostly bitumen, but it may also contain asphalt or tar. Asphalt is derived from petroleum, tars from coal. Tars are advantageous where resistance to gasoline or other fuels is desirable since they are not dissolved by fuels, as asphalt is. Thus, tar surfaces offer resistance to gasoline spills or airfields, to fluid leaks on parking lots, and so on. However, tar malleability varies a great deal with temperature changes, so that the tar may become too soft in tropical or semi-tropical climates and too brittle in cold climates. Local authorities usually have data for recommended mixtures, surface treatments, etc.

Mix Plants

Different paving jobs require different mixtures of bituminous paving, depending largely on the frequency and type of traffic that will be present. Thus, temporary roads, such as highway detours, county roads with light traffic, driveways, etc., need not be built to stand the punishment of airfields, highly used expressways, bridges, and the like. Accordingly, mix plants are established to produce the level of quality that is consistent with project needs. Broadly, a given mix plant is either (1) a high-type plant, (2) an intermediate-type plant, or (3) a soil treatment plant.

High-type, or multiple-aggregate, mix plants produce mixes that are suitable for major highways, airfields, and similar heavy-duty surfaces. High-type plants use equipment that is capable of very accurately separating and mixing sands, gravels, and fines. High-type plants also may be used for intermediate-type mixes. Thus, where both high- and intermediate-grade surfaces are needed, it is common to use the high-type plant.

Intermediate-type, or single-aggregate, plants produce mixes that are suitable for average traffic conditions. Materials handling equipment is not as sophisticated in this type of plant, and mixing is not as accurate as in the high type. However, the simplicity of the plant and the minimization of materials handling effect cost savings where the intermediate-mix surface is adequate.

Soil treatment plants produce material for some base courses and for certain light-duty surfaces. There is little materials handling in this plant and absolutely no control over aggregate gradation.

Mix plants may be further classified as *batch plants* or *continuous-mix plants*. Batch plants utilize a mix chamber to mix weighed proportions of mix ingredients. When the ingredients are mixed, the product must be entirely removed before the next batch of ingredients is introduced.

Conversely, the continuous-mix plant measures ingredients in a weight-volume relationship. Thus, the ingredients may be introduced continuously into the system, from entry to discharge, thereby producing a uniform mixture.

CONCRETE PLANTS

Concrete surfaces are excellent for almost any type of traffic and amount of use. Concrete makes for a durable surface that is skid resistant and smooth. But it is an expensive surface and thus is not used where asphalt will suffice. That is, concrete is seldom used on ground-level parking lots, temporary roads, light-duty roads, etc. It has, of course, many uses other than as a pavement; it is used, e.g., for foundations, structural members, masonry, bridges, and more.

Mix Plants

As with asphalt production, concrete may be produced by batch or continuous-mix plants. Batch plants are of two varieties: *aggregate batching* and *cement batching*. The aggregate batching plant proportions the sand and gravel used in the concrete mix, whereas the cement batching plant proportions the amount of cement used per batch of concrete.

Central Mix Plant

The concrete central mix plant batches and mixes concrete in a continuous operation.

Large asphalt and concrete plants are a special branch of the construction business. Therefore, they have not been discussed in depth in this text. Rather, the discussion has focused on making the reader aware of the quality of product that is typical of the different operations. Similarly, small asphalt and concrete producing machines (such as drum mixers) and tools have not been discussed. For in-depth discussions of these items, the reader is directed to standard texts on the subjects.

The following equipment is frequently used by fairly small to large-scale contractors.

CRAWLER-MOUNTED ASPHALT PAVER

The crawler-mounted asphalt paver has two main components: the tractor unit and the screed unit. The tractor pulls the screed unit and pushes the truck that hauls the asphalt mix. The screed unit strikes or "screeds" the asphalt at the proper level and provides the initial compaction; compactors do the final compaction. (See Figure 9–1.)

Typically, these pavers are equipped with an automatic control system that monitors and maintains the screed level at the desired height. Towed pavers may be used for smaller jobs, and special shoulder pavers are available which may be attached to other equipment, such as motor graders. Self-propelled machines are also available.

THE ASPHALT CRUSHER

The asphalt crusher is used in recycling existing asphalt paving. It is available in a portable (wheeled) unit and a stationary (skid-mounted) unit.

Source: Barber-Greene

Figure 9–1. Crawler-mounted asphalt paver. This machine maintains screed level automatically. It is suitable for jobs 8 to 36 feet wide.

(See Figure 9–2.) The main components of the machine are the feeder/hopper, a special crusher, and the discharge conveyor. These components are mounted on a chassis which in turn may be wheel- or skid-mounted.

The machine shown in the figure will produce approximately 200–400 tons per hour. Considerable materials savings are possible with this machine where existing asphalt paving must be removed.

CRAWLER-MOUNTED ASPHALT COLD PLANER

The cold planer is used to plane down roads, correcting existing poor surfaces and/or preparing them for resurfacing; to excavate existing pavement, down to (and including, if necessary) the subgrade; and to excavate and pulverize existing pavement, utilizing the existing materials for resurfacing. (See Figure 9–3.) Basic components of the machine include the crawler mounting, a (bidirectional) planing drum, and a conveyor system.

The machine is typically used for city street and county road reclamation, highway restoration, parking lots, runways, etc. Where project demands allow, it may be used to cold-recycle surfaces by removing and pulverizing the existing pavement, to which a new binding agent is added, and then spreading, compacting, and sealing the material with either a surface treatment or an overlay.

Figure 9–2. Asphalt crusher. These machines are used to reclaim the materials that would otherwise be lost when existing asphalt paving is removed.

Source: Barber-Greene   (a)

Source: Barber-Greene   (b)

Figure 9–3. (a) Asphalt cold planer discharging materials into truck. (b) Cold planer may also be used to remove and pulverize existing materials for immediate reuse.

CONCRETEMOBILE

The concretemobile shown in Figure 9–4 (Barber–Greene Company) was designed to consolidate the functions of truck mixers and portable concrete plants, thus reducing the amount of equipment and labor needed on a given job. The machine is typically wheel mounted, but crawler mountings are available for rough terrain. Other components include:

1. Separate compartments for sand, aggregate, and cement
2. Water tanks
3. Two containers for carrying liquid admixtures (accelerators, retarders, air entraining agents, etc.)
4. A feeder which proportions cement into the mix at a constant rate
5. Adjustable flow gates at the rear of the machine
6. Flow meters for monitoring admixture and water flow rates
7. An integral conveyor belt which transports materials to the water and admixture station, and hence through an auger which may be hydraulically raised, lowered, and swiveled to deposit the concrete where desired

Concretemobiles may be used for a wide range of job sizes in commercial, industrial, residential, and agricultural construction.

CONCRETE SLIPFORM MACHINE

The concrete slipform machine is frequently used for curbs and gutters, barrier walls, valley gutters, trenches, outside pours, and slabs up to 8 feet wide. Other configurations are also possible.

Slipform machines are crawler mounted. Concrete is fed through the machine to the screed system. (See Figure 9–5.)

(a)

(b)

Figure 9–4. Concretemobiles are practical for a wide range of job sizes and types.

(c)

(d)

Figure 9–4. (Continued).

Source: Barber-Greene (a)

Source: Barber-Greene (b)

Figure 9–5. Slipformers are frequently used for (a) outside pours, (b) barrier walls, and (c) slabs up to 8 feet wide. Valley gutters, trenches, and other shapes are possible.

(c)

Figure 9–5. (Continued).

10

CONCRETE FORMING

DESIGNING FORMS

The architect or engineer dictates much of the form requirements by virtue of the structure's design. Experienced architects and engineers try to avoid designs that cause cost problems. Typically, for example, they avoid structural members that require special fabrication or cutting in cases where standard sizes and shapes will perform and function just as well. Similarly, they avoid structural shapes that increase the difficulty of building concrete structures. Formwork is an important cost item for concrete structures; it should be simplified wherever possible to reduce costs.

This is not to say, however, that formwork or even cost determines design and aesthetics. Architects often elect to increase cost to achieve some aesthetic effect: a pattern on a wall or plaza, a striking curvilinear shape, etc. But experienced professionals know costs and know that they must set priorities and make compromises to achieve the best structures possible within reasonable cost for their functions. The designing of formwork, then, follows the design of the structure, although architects and engineers frequently call on knowledgeable constructors for advice about building methods and cost efficiency.

Specifically, architects and engineers may reduce formwork costs by:

1. Consulting with constructors at the preliminary design stage and as the project progresses.

2. Designing structures so that standard formwork materials and shapes may be used to the maximum extent practicable. To do so requires a working knowledge of the type and shape of formwork available from manufacturers, as well as of the type of formwork that can usually be built at the job site by most constructors.

3. Designing so that the simplest forms may be used and so that the forms may be used repetitively, thus minimizing the amount of formwork needed—fabricated, preengineered metal or synthetic pans for forming roof decks and joists, for example.

4. Integrating the formwork with the structure—metal roof decking, for example, where the corrugated metal is both a form and a permanent part of the structure.

The following discussion of form design and materials is about one of today's most frequently used systems.

Plywood Forms for Walls and Columns

Plywood is a frequently used formwork material. Much site-built formwork is built with it, and many manufacturers of forms use it.

Plywood has good insulating qualities. Thin panels can be used for curvilinear forms in combination with metal and/or wood backing. Plywood is available in many surface textures and patterns, including very smooth surfaces. The American Plywood Association (APA) has established grades of plywood, and many of the exterior grades are suitable for formwork. Two classes, however, PLYFORM I and PLYFORM II, are manufactured specifically for formwork. PLYFORM I has the greater strength and stiffness.

All formwork must be designed to resist *concrete pressure*. The required plywood thickness, size, and spacing of framing lumber depends on the maximum amount of concrete pressure the formwork must be able to withstand. Therefore, the first step in form design is to determine this pressure. For column and wall forms, factors to consider include the pour rate of concrete, the temperature at the job site, concrete slump, the type of cement used, concrete density, the method of vibration, and the form height.

Many combinations of framing sizes and plywood thicknesses are possible. However, it is simplest to use one thickness of plywood (where practicable) and vary the spacing of the framing to accommodate different pressures. The APA suggests using ⅝- or ¾-inch PLYFORM Class I. Again, thinner plywood formwork may possibly be used; however, the most cost-effective formwork is not necessarily designed by stressing all the formwork members to their maximum allowable loads, because ease of construction (with its attendant lower labor costs) is also a factor in cost. Further, the initial formwork design may be modified as experience on the job brings new possibilities to light.

The problem set out in this discussion is to design a wall form where (1) internally vibrated concrete will be placed in the wall forms at the rate of 3 feet per hour, and (2) the temperature is 70 degrees. We are to (1) find the maximum support spacing for ⅝-inch PLYFORM Class I plywood for an architectural concrete wall that is 9 feet high, and (2) select the framing and ties for the wall.

Find the Maximum Concrete Pressure. Table 10–1 shows that 540 pounds per square foot (psf) of pressure is required for a temperature of 70 degrees and a pour rate of 3 feet per hour.

Table 10–2a shows the allowable pressures for PLYFORM that is placed with its face grain across the wall supports. We shall assume this to be the case in our discussion. (See Table 10–2b for the allowable pressures for PLYFORM with its face grain parallel to the wall supports.)

The allowable pressures in the tables are for PLYFORM for architectural applications, in psf; deflection is limited to 1/360th of the span for plywood that is continuous across two or more spans. Plywood grades other than PLYFORM Class I can be used for forms for which a minimum number of reuses is required, or to produce special textured effects in the concrete. PLYFORM Class II, or textured panels in species group 1 or 2, will carry approximately the same loads as PLYFORM Class I if the panels are ⅛ inch thicker than those of the Class I.

Table 10–1. Concrete Pressures for Column and Wall Forms.

POUR RATE (FT/HR)	CONCRETE PRESSURES (psf) (a)(b)(c)			
	WALLS(d)		COLUMNS(d)	
	50°	70°	50°	70°
2	510	410	510	410
3	690	540	690	540
4	870	660	870	660
5	1050	790	1050	790
6	1230	920	1230	920
7	1410	1050	1410	1050
8	1470	1090	1590	1180
9	1520	1130	1770	1310
10	1580	1170	1950	1440

For ordinary work with normal internal vibration in columms:

$$P = 150 + 9,000 \frac{R}{T} \text{ (maximum 3,000 psf or 150h, whichever is less)}$$

For ordinary work with normal internal vibration in walls (rate of placement not greater than 7 ft per hour):

$$P = 150 + 9,000 \frac{R}{T} \text{(maximum 2,000 psf or 150h, whichever is less)}$$

For ordinary work with normal internal vibration in walls with rate of placement greater than 7 ft per hour:

$$P = 150 + \frac{43,400}{T} + 2,800 \frac{R}{T} \text{(maximum 2,000 psf or 150h, whichever is less)}$$

Where: P = lateral pressure in lb per sq ft.
R = rate of placement, ft per hour.
T = temperature of concrete in the forms, °F.
h = height of fresh concrete above point considered, ft.

(a) Maximum design pressure need not exceed 150h, where h is maximum height of pour.
(b) For unvibrated concrete, design pressure may be decreased 10 percent.
(c) Test data indicate possible variation in concrete pressures due to temperature, rate of pour, water-cement ratio, admixtures, etc. Suggested design pressures shown are recommended only as general guidelines, and are based on American Concrete Institute formulas.
(d) For other temperatures and rates of pour, ACI recommends the equations shown above.

FOR SLAB PRESSURE: Figure 12½ psf per inch of concrete depth, plus a surcharge to allow for placing equipment. For nonmotorized buggies, use at least 50 psf uniform load surcharge and at least 75 psf for motorized buggies.

Table 10–2a. Wood Grain Across Supports.

SUPPORT SPACING (INCHES)	PLYWOOD THICKNESS (INCHES)					
	1/2	5/8	3/4	7/8	1	1-1/8
4	3265	4095	5005	5225	5650	6290
8	970	1300	1650	2005	2175	2420
12	410	575	735	890	1190	1400
16	175	270	370	475	645	750
20	100	160	225	295	410	490
24			120	160	230	280
32					105	130
36						115

Table 10–2b. Wood Grain Parallel to Supports.

SUPPORT SPACING (INCHES)	PLYWOOD THICKNESS (INCHES)					
	1/2	5/8	3/4	7/8	1	1-1/8
4	1860	2350	2910	3540	4615	5455
8	605	905	1120	1325	1775	2100
12	215	360	670	820	1100	1300
16		150	300	480	725	895
20		105	210	290	400	495
24			110	180	255	320

Determine the maximum support spacing for PLYFORM. Look down the column in Table 10–2a for ⅝-inch PLYFORM. It shows 575 psf for supports at 12 inches on center. Therefore, use 12-inch maximum support spacing even though a slightly greater support spacing is permissible.

Design the Studs. Since the plywood must be supported at 12 inches on center, space all studs thus. The load carried by each stud equals the concrete pressure multiplied by the stud spacing, in feet, i.e.,

$$540 \text{ psf} \times \frac{12}{12} \text{ ft} = 540 \text{ lb/ft}$$

Assuming 2×6 studs continuously over 3 supports (2 spans), Table 10–3 shows a 53-inch span for 400 lb/ft and a 43-inch span for 600 lb/ft. Interpolating between these span is for a load of 540 lb/ft yields

$$\frac{540 - 400}{600 - 400} \times (53 - 43) = \frac{140}{200} \times (10) = 7 \text{ inches}$$

Table 10–3. Maximum Spans for Lumber Framing in Inches, Douglas Fir-larch No. 2, Southern Pine No. 2 Medium Grain (19%), or an Equivalent Wood.

EQUIVALENT UNIFORM LOAD (LB/FT)	CONTINUOUS OVER 2 OR 3 SUPPORTS (1 OR 2 SPANS)								CONTINUOUS OVER 4 OR MORE SUPPORTS (3 OR MORE SPANS)							
	NOMINAL SIZE								NOMINAL SIZE							
	2×4	2×6	2×8	2×10	2×12	4×4	4×6	4×8	2×4	2×6	2×8	2×10	2×12	4×4	4×6	4×8
400	36	53	70	90	109	50	79	101	41	60	78	100	122	62	91	118
600	30	43	57	73	89	44	66	88	31	49	64	82	99	51	74	98
800	24	38	50	63	77	39	58	76	25	39	52	66	81	44	64	85
1000	21	33	43	55	67	35	51	68	21	34	44	57	69	39	58	76
1200	19	29	38	49	60	32	47	62	19	30	39	50	61	35	53	69
1400	17	27	35	45	54	30	43	57	17	27	36	46	56	31	49	64
1600	16	25	32	41	50	27	41	54	16	25	33	42	52	28	44	58
1800	15	23	30	39	47	25	38	51	15	24	31	40	48	26	40	53
2000	14	22	29	37	45	23	36	48	14	22	29	38	46	24	37	49
2500	13	20	26	33	40	20	31	41	13	20	26	34	41	20	32	42
3000	12	18	24	31	37	18	28	37	12	19	24	31	38	18	29	38
4000	10	16	22	28	34	15	24	31	11	17	22	28	34	15	24	32
5000	10	15	20	25	31	13	21	28	10	16	20	26	32	14	22	28

Thus, for 540 lb/ft, the span is 53 inches minus 7 inches = 46 inches. Accordingly, the 2×6 studs must be supported at 46 inches on center. We shall assume that this support is provided by double 2×6 wales spaced 46 inches on center.

Design the Double Wales. The load carried by the double wales equals the maximum concrete pressure multiplied by the wale spacing in feet, or

$$540 \text{ psf} \times \frac{46}{12} \text{ ft} = 2,070 \text{ lb/ft}$$

Since the wales are doubled, each wale carries 1,035 lb/ft (2,070 ÷ 2 = 1,035). Assuming 2×6 wales continuous over four or more supports, Table 10–3 shows a 30-inch span for 1,200 lb/ft. Interpolation shows that 2×6s can span approximately 33 inches for 1,035 lb/ft. Accordingly, support the 2×6s at 33 inches on center with form ties. (Place the bottom wale about 8 inches from the bottom of the form.)

The spans in Table 10–3 are based on PS-20 lumber sizes. Single-member stresses were multiplied by a 1.25 duration-of-load factor for 7-day loads; deflection was limited to $\frac{1}{360}$th of the span with $\frac{1}{4}$ inch maximum. Spans are center to center of the supports.

Load on the Ties. The load on each tie equals the load on the double wales times the tie spacing in feet, or

$$2{,}070 \text{ lb/ft} \times \frac{33}{12} \text{ ft} = 5{,}690 \text{ lb}$$

If the allowable load on the tie is less than 5,690 lb, decrease the tie spacing accordingly. For instance, a tie with a 5,000-lb allowable load should have spacing no more than

$$\frac{5{,}000}{2{,}070} \times 12 \text{ in} = 29 \text{ in}$$

Other Loads on Forms. Provide adequate diagonal bracing for wind loads and other externally applied loads. Figure 10–1 illustrates a typical wall form arrangement.

The constructor can further economize formwork for well-designed structures by observing the following simple guidelines:

1. Develop working drawings. Initially, working drawings aid the estimator in figuring more accurate cost data, and thus more accurate

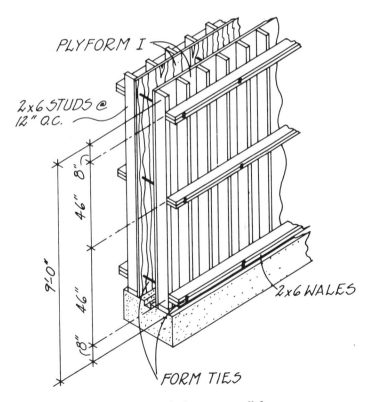

Figure 10–1. Typical concrete wall form.

bids and profit estimates are possible. Further, working drawings tend to produce formwork that is neither overdesigned nor underdesigned. (Overdesigned forms are expensive, and underdesigned forms may be dangerous.) Finally, working drawings cut down on job site errors and reduce the amount of direct supervision needed to build the forms.

2. Think of the entire job, including the formwork, as a manufacturing system. Provide a convenient workspace, on the ground where practicable (building the forms on the ground is usually faster than building them on scaffolding), and break the work down into simple tasks similar to factory tasks.

3. When selecting the type of forms and form material(s), consider the use of the forms, if any, beyond the current job. Initial cost is important, but if the forms can be used on several more jobs in the near future, longer lasting forms may eventually yield greater profits.

4. Consider renting forms. Renting forms, particularly when no future use is foreseen, can increase profits.

5. Whether renting or buying, use the minimum number of forms necessary to keep the job moving continuously. To do this usually requires carefully planned construction joints: construction is interrupted at the joints, the forms are removed from previous work and reinstalled, construction is resumed, and so on. Engineering and architectural approval of the joint design and location are usually required.

6. Use prefabricated forms if they are cheaper. The job size and construction schedule will be two important factors to consider. Time is very important in construction, as labor is a major cost. Thus, if the job is large enough, the time saved by using manufactured forms with convenient accessories, ties, etc., may be worth the initial cost of the forms.

7. Keep the forms in use. The amount of time the forms must remain on the concrete is usually noted in the specifications. Do not let the forms remain on any longer than necessary.

8. Maintain the forms. The material usually dictates the kind of maintenance needed. Forms should always be cleaned after removal. Also, it is sometimes necessary to oil the forms before and after use.

9. Do not oversecure the forms. Too many nails weaken lumber and increase the difficulty of removing the forms. Consider double-headed nails or scaffold nails for easy removal.

10. Use simple, modular forms wherever possible. Even curvilinear shapes can be divided into mostly rectangular or regular form

shapes. The remaining areas must of course utilize custom forms, often built at the job site. Always minimize the use of these custom forms, however.

11. Use the largest form sizes practicable. Power euqipment is needed to lift large forms into position, but this method is usually cheaper and faster than building smaller forms and installing them with manpower, except on small jobs. For small jobs, where manpower is used to set the forms in place, the size of the forms will be largely determined by their weight: workers should not have to handle unsafe loads, especially at awkward angles or under other difficult working conditions.

FORM MATERIALS

Wood is the most typical formwork material, and plywood is probably used more often than wood planks. Where constructors can foresee much use of a particular form, metal should be considered, since it will take more abuse than wood and last longer. Aluminum forms have the advantage of being lightweight. For example, one worker can handle a fairly large deck form or a similar form. Steel forms require more manpower and/or power equipment to handle them. On large projects the weight factor may not be as significant as on smaller projects (or smaller units, such as houses), as the forms are usually ganged and lifted with power equipment. Thus, the choice between wood or metal forms depends mostly on how much the forms will be used. The choice between steel forms and aluminum forms depends largely on project size and installation methods.

KINDS OF FORMS

Footing Forms. Metal footing forms are particularly attractive to residential and light construction builders, where the footings are the same or very similar. For example, in a subdivision, many, if not all, of the footings would be very similar. Wood forms could be used repetitively, but metal forms would last longer.

Edge Forms. Slab edges, like residential footings, are often very similar. Drive edges, floor slabs, sidewalks, and similar construction lend themselves to repetitive form use. Metal footing forms sometimes double as edge forms.

Concrete Blocks Used as Forms. Concrete blocks are frequently used to double for formwork, especially in light construction. Typically, the hollow cells are used to house reinforcing steel, and the blocks are then filled with concrete. Columns, bond beams, pilasters, and similar components are often formed in this manner.

Joist Pans. Joist pans are a frequently used, economical forming system. Office buildings, parking garages, institutional buildings, and a wide variety of other structures are often formed with manufactured joist pans. The joist pan system also can be used economically for a relatively wide range of project sizes.

The pans are typically made of metal or fiberglass. There are basically two shapes: long, rectangular pans, and square or nearly square "waffle" forms. The long forms are used for one-way joist construction; the waffle forms are for two-way joist construction. (See Figure 10–2.)

Joist pans require a temporary platform on which to rest until the poured concrete can support itself. The platform may be metal or wood trusses or scaffolding, or any appropriate support system. The pans rest on ledges, typically wood, which in turn rest on the temporary support system.

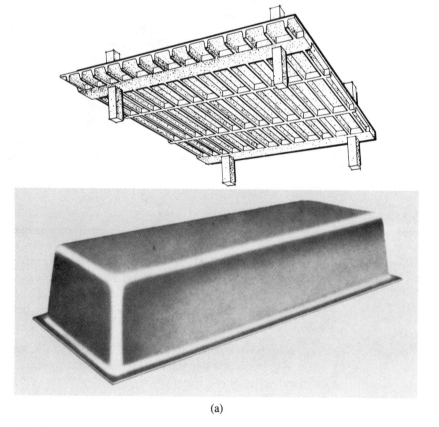

(a)

Figure 10–2. (a) One-way joist construction. Pan is a long, rectangular shape.

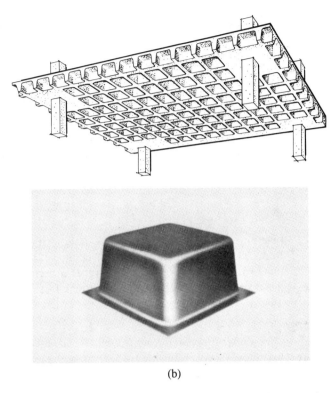

(b)

Figure 10–2. (Continued). (b) Two-way joist construction. Pan form is square or nearly square. Source: Ceco Corporation.

Beam-and-Slab Forms. Beam-and-slab formwork is relatively simple. Typical job site lumber is often used, usually plywood sheathing with 2-inch lumber framework. Figure 10–3 shows a beam-and-slab floor. The beam forms are simply trough shapes of plywood and supporting 2-inch framework. The floor formwork is plywood with supporting framework as required. The formwork is typically held up with tubular-steel scaffolding, which will be discussed shortly.

Flat Plate Forms. A flat plate floor is shown in Figure 10–4. These slabs use steel reinforcement for their structural strength; there are no joists or beams to be formed, since the slab is tied directly to the columns. Thus, the form required is simply a flat platform, typically made with plywood sheathing over 2-inch lumber, similar to the beam-and-slab form just discussed. Flat plate formwork l_ _s much like a section of residential flooring (plywood over regularly spaced wood joists). The formwork is typically supported with tubular-steel scaffolding (see below).

Steel Floor and Roof Forms. Corrugated steel floor and roof forms are frequently used in light construction. The steel forms are usually used in com-

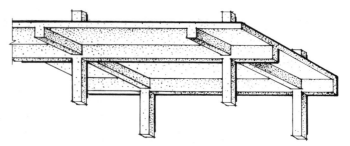

Figure 10–3. Beam-and-slab floor.

bination with open-web steel joists. Laid at right angles to the joists, the steel forms (1) contribute to structural rigidity, (2) provide a convenient working platform for workers, and (3) serve as a permenant form for concrete floors and roofs. Using steel forms makes for a fast method of building. (See Figure 10–5.)

Other Floor and Roof Forms. Besides the typical corrugated metal decking shape shown in Figure 10–5, there are many other shapes available for specific needs—to house mechanical, plumbing, and electrical equipment; to provide space for insulation; and to accommodate other particular building needs. Indeed, sometimes precast structural and semistructural units (such as solid concrete reinforced planks and cellular concrete reinforced planks) are laid over the supporting system, and then a concrete topping is poured to finish the surface.

Many materials have been used for permanent formwork for concrete floors and roofs.

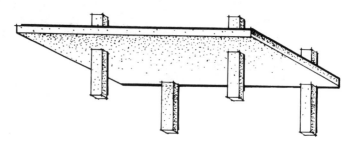

Figure 10–4. Flat plate floor.

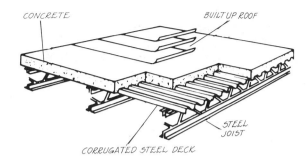

CONCRETE   BUILT UP ROOF

STEEL
JOIST

CORRUGATED STEEL DECK

Figure 10–5. Corrugated steel used as form for roof deck.

SHORES AND TUBULAR-STEEL SCAFFOLDING

Shores are temporary vertical supports used to hold formwork in place until the concrete is capable of supporting itself. They may be made of metal or wood, or a combination of these materials. (See Figure 10–6.)

Tubular-steel scaffolding employs steel pipe to build support modules. A single module is similar in appearance to a metal bunk bed. The modules may be stacked to almost any practical height for building purposes. Each particular module size will have a safe height and load capacity. For supporting formwork at significant heights, ''columns'' of scaffolding may be connected horizontally to increase stability. (See Figure 10–7.)

RECTANGULAR COLUMNS

Rectangular columns are probably most frequently formed with plywood, although wood planks, which are slower to install, are still used. The forms may be held together with wood members, but adjustable metal clamps are faster to install and easier to remove.

Typical columns for light construction and even most heavy jobs are hand set. Very large columns, bridge piers, and similar vertical members are more economically installed by gang forming with power equipment.

Completely prefabricated forms and accessories for rectangular columns are available from manufacturers. These forms are often plywood with a steel framework. Metal clamps, wedge bolts, and other time-saving devices usually eliminate most or all nailing.

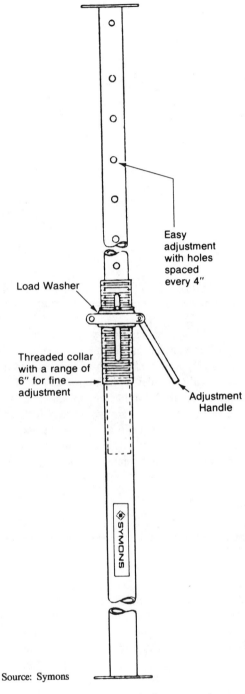

Easy
adjustment
with holes
spaced
every 4"

Load Washer

Threaded collar
with a range of
6" for fine
adjustment

Adjustment
Handle

SYMONS

Source: Symons

Figure 10–6. Metal post shore. Wood shores are also available, as are combination wood and metal shores.

154

Figure10–7. Tubular-steel scaffolding with adjustable posts.

ROUND COLUMNS

Round columns are difficult to form on the job. Thus, where a fair number of round columns will be required, prefabricated column forms are usually used. These forms are frequently made of fiber and are stripped away when the concrete has set. Metal and fiberglass forms are seeing increased use, especially on large jobs. Such forms are clamped or bolted together and may be used indefinitely.

TILT-UP CONSTRUCTION

Tilt-up construction most often means tilt-up wall panels. However, other building components such as columns, beams, and roof components may be built using the tilt-up method. Simply put, tilt-up construction is a method of job site prefabrication. As the name implies, the wall panels or other components are formed on the ground and then tilted or lifted into place.

Tilt-up construction can be a fast, economical building system. However, it is not as simple as it may appear to someone watching a building being erected by means of its methodology. The reason for this is that in order for the actual erection to achieve its goals of speed and economy, the tilt-up method must be preceded by very careful designing and planning work.

The floor slab of the building usually serves as the casting surface for the tilt-up wall panels. Thus, it is important to schedule the work so that the floor slab is installed as quickly as possible. Using the floor slab to cast the tilt-up wall panels gives an immediate cost advantage because the floor doubles as part of the formwork. Of course the edges of the panels still need formwork of wood or metal, and formwork is needed for any door, window, or other opening in the wall panels. But, obviously, the elimination of the vertical formwork normally used for cast-in-place walls makes for considerable savings.

Before the tilt-up panels are poured on the floor slab, precautions must be taken to ensure that the panel pours do not bond to the floor slab. Chemical compounds are available for this purpose, and paper or canvas is sometimes used between the panel pours and the floor slab.

The tilt-up panels contain reinforcing steel that serves the structural needs of the building and prevents damage to the panels when they are lifted into position by power equipment. The panels are fitted with steel pick-up devices imbedded in the panel in coordination with the reinforcing steel; these devices become the pick-up units of the panel. There may be two, four, six, or even more pick-up units per panel, depending on the size and weight of the panels, the number and size of openings, and other factors.

The tilt-up panels are usually lifted into position with a crane which holds them in place while workers erect temporary bracing to secure them. The bracing may be wood or metal and should be designed before erection begins. The size of the crane needed depends on the weight and size of the panels and the physical working conditions of the site. On small buildings, and in cases where the wall panels are formed at or very near the place they will be installed, backhoes are sometimes used for placement of the panels.

Vacuum lifters are sometimes used to lift and position the panels. The vacuum lifter fits against the wall panels and is secured to the panel for lifting by means of a mat and vacuum pump. Vacuum lifters have been used successfully for precast and factory-produced concrete components but have seen less success in typical tilt-up projects. The reason for this is that smaller the job, the less economical the vacuum lifter usually is.

Planning a tilt-up project intensifies the normal need for close coordination of architectural, engineering, and construction activities. Tilt-up jobs gain economy largely by speed of erection, which can unfortunately quickly be lost by lack of coordination. Also, mistakes in tilt-up panels are more difficult to deal with than mistakes in conventional walls.

The end result of planning a tilt-up job is usually a *casting plan*. The casting plan is similar in appearance to the floor plan but is less detailed because the purpose of the casting plan is to show the location and method of erection of all wall panels and other fabricated components that affect the flow of the work. The casting plan indicates work traffic patterns, erection sequence, storage facilities, and other factors. For foremen, workers, and others involved, it may be necessary to build a scale model of the project, using cardboard and/or balsa wood to represent the actual building and tilt-up panels and other components.

SLIP FORMS

Slip forms get their name because they are slipped up the structures they form while the concrete is still somewhat plastic. A tall concrete chimney stack or a silo, for example, could be built using slip forms. The form is poured, the concrete is allowed to set a specified period, the form is moved up for the next pour, and so forth, until the structure is completed. Obviously, slip forms are only practical on rather uniformly shaped structures, such as those mentioned above and bridge piers, high-rise buildings, and other structures with similar shape characteristics. Also, the structures must be tall enough to justify the use of the slip form system.

Great care must be taken in checking the concrete as the forms are lifted. If the forms are lifted too quickly, before the concrete has adequately set, the concrete will bulge out, causing a deformation and possibly damage to the structure. If the forms are allowed to set too long, the concrete may stick to them. Regular inspection by a qualified concrete inspector is required to assure the correct rate of concrete setting, uniform form lifting, and proper form maintenance. For really large structures, such as high-rise buildings, towers, etc., many constructors elect to rent or buy forms from formwork manufacturers, who offer support specialists for consultation on the specific formwork system employed.

Slip forms are typically lifted with hydraulic jacks, although manually operated screw jacks may be used. In either case, the jacks must lift the forms uniformly to keep the wall structure vertical. Thus, hydraulic jacks are less cumbersome because they automatically lift all the jacks uniformly.

SLIPFORM PAVING

The relatively uniform cross sections of streets, walks, medians, curbs, and gutters are ideal for slipform construction. Accordingly, special paving machines have been developed that can lay over a mile of street pavement per day. Some machines are even equipped to lay curbs and gutters as integral parts of the street, further reducing the time of construction. The formwork is a part of the machine, and as the machine moves, the concrete laid maintains its shape without requiring more forms. Also, since slipform paving machines are not hampered by reinforcing steel, reinforcing work may be conducted well ahead of the machine. After the concrete is laid, workers follow behind and do the work that remains, such as joint cutting, any remaining finish or curing work, etc. The machines, therefore, are highly efficient, because with workers both ahead and behind of the machine, there is little wasted time.

Some machines are equipped to do almost all the work, from compacting soil, grade trimming, and surface finishing to curing and concrete (and asphalt) laying.

WALL FORM BRACING

Wall forms must be securely braced, both for safety and to prevent damage to the walls. On small jobs, scrap lumber may sometimes be used economically. But in general, the larger the job, the more standardized and simple the bracing must be; otherwise, more money is spent on labor and time lost to building the braces than would be spent on standard bracing members.

Bracing may be metal or wood or a combination of the two and should be adjustable. Well-constructed formwork need only be braced on one side, since the formwork walls are secured together. (See Figure 10–8.)

TIES

When the concrete is poured, considerable outward pressure is generated against the wall forms. Thus, steel ties are used to keep the wall forms from bulging. There are many types and strengths of steel ties. Figure 10–9 illustrates two of them.

FORM FINISHES AND FORM LINERS

Concrete assumes the same finish appearance as the form it is poured against. Concrete poured between wall forms of rough-sawn planks, for example, will take on the grain appearance and texture of the planks, the joints between the planks, the nail heads, and indeed, everything that is on the planks.

Rough-sawn plank formwork is sometimes chosen because that is the finish that is desired. At other times, the designer may want a finish as nearly perfectly smooth as possible. The desired finish is an aesthetic consideration that also has cost consequences. Rough-sawn planks, for example, could often cost more to install than plywood forms; but if the finish requirements were met at the same time, then the total cost could be less if such planks are used.

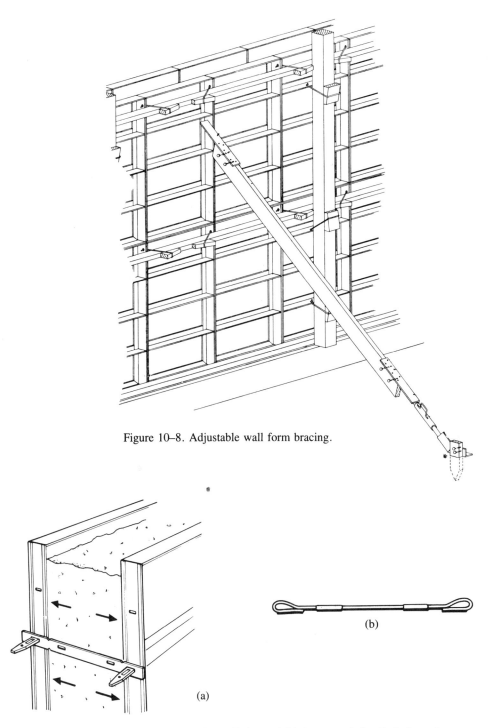

Figure 10–8. Adjustable wall form bracing.

Figure 10–9. (a) Flat wall tie, and (b) loop panel tie. Both these ties are frequently used.

Conversely, if a smooth surface were desired, the cost of very smooth plywood might pay for itself by reducing the amount of finish work needed to smooth the surface after form removal.

Thus, the natural form material surface may sometimes be used to create the concrete wall finish. Sometimes, also, the wall form materials are further treated by sand blasting, by adding joint patterns, or by similar physical alterations that will show up on the concrete walls. Some form materials, such as aluminum or fiberglass, are made to simulate the appearance of brick, stone, flagstone, planks, etc., which will be transferred to the concrete wall.

Another way to create concrete wall finishes is to use form liners. Form liners are made of either plastic, fiberglass, urethane, or materials with similar characteristics and are secured to the inside of the form walls before the concrete is poured. When the concrete is finally poured, it assumes the shape and texture of the liner, typically either wood grains, planks, vertical or horizontal ribbed patterns, stone or masonry, or specially designed sculptural patterns.

The best finishing solution requires careful consideration of the desired finish, reuse of forms and/or form liners, and evaluation of the cost of materials and labor to install the forms, as well as any other cost factors.

COST

According to one form manufacturer, formwork labor and materials can account for 30 to almost 50% of the total cost of building concrete walls. Indeed, the cost of labor has become more significant than the cost of form materials (and some other building materials as well). Thus, any labor-saving device is worth considering. Further, the more repetitive use the forms see, the less significant the initial material cost becomes. Constructors who build their own forms must estimate the cost of materials, usually including plywood sheathing; framing lumber; any steel angles or other steel used plus welding costs, if any; nails; bolts; wedge bolts; wall ties; form connectors; and miscellaneous hardware and materials. *Labor cost* is the number of man-hours required to erect the forms and remove them later.

If the forms cannot be salvaged after the job is completed, or if little or no reuse of the forms is anticipated, the cost of the materials will of course be high. In such cases, constructors usually should consider renting the forms. If, on the other hand, the constructor can reuse the forms, the cost of the materials drops quickly. The decision then becomes whether to build the forms on the job or obtain them from a manufacturer. The choice then depends on the skills available to the constructor. Form manufacturing is a specialized business, and not all constructors can economically build their own forms, even if reuse is a certainty. Thus, many constructors purchase their formwork from manufacturers who assume the responsibilities of designing and building the formwork for the constructor's needs and who also may contract to install the formwork and/or remove it later. In some cases, a lease–purchase option is available. This option lowers initial investment, and, in time, the constructor owns the forms.

11

SAFETY

The first and most important aspect of safety on the job is of course the prevention of job-related accidents and deaths. Not only may job-related accidents be tragic, but, from the company's point of view, they are very expensive: they increase insurance costs and create costly construction delays. Moreover, various authorities demand that certain safety standards be met. For example, the Federal Occupational Safety and Health Act (OSHA) sets forth a system of safety regulations, record keeping, and inspections, violations of which can result in serious fines and even imprisonment. Insurance companies also may have safety requirements. None of the authorities are interested in making construction more difficult, and they are not eager to levy penalties. They are interested, however, in reducing accidents that bring legal suits and increase costs to the industry.

SAFETY PROGRAMS

Each type of construction has hazards and safety demands that are peculiar to it. Further, safety requirements vary geographically: those of Alaska, for example, differ somewhat from those of Florida. Finally, each job and each piece of equipment will have its own particular safety requirements. Therefore, it is not possible to assemble a safety program that will apply to the whole construction industry. Rather, a satisfactory safety program must be devised for each contractor that suits the particulars of the work being done and the equipment and personnel used to do it.

Certain requirements, however, are common to all organizations and all safety programs. The following list includes some of the more important safety program preliminaries:

1. All safety programs must have the *active* support of top management, and safety supervisors must be designated.

2. Proper equipment must be provided, e.g., protective clothing, fire extinguishers, rollover protective structures (ROPs) for equipment, first aid equipment, etc.

3. Safety must be impressed and maintained in the minds of employees. Regularly administered safety courses should be used. New employees should complete a safety course before going to work, and all employees should attend regular refresher courses.

4. Safety records must be established and maintained, and regular safety inspections must be provided.

5. A plan for dealing with injuries must be established, including the provision of a first-aid facility and transportation to the appropriate medical facility.

Fortunately, there are many good sources of safety information from which safety programs may be designed. Insurance companies can provide good safety information. Established contractors and contracting associations can lend valuable advice. The Society of Automotive Engineers (SAE) has established safety criteria, as has OSHA. The Mine Safety and Health Administration (MSHA) administers safety regulations for mining operations. The American National Standards Institute (ANSI) has established safety standards. The Construction Industry Manufacturers Association (CIMA), through its bureau, the Power Crane and Shovel Association, has assembled safety information standards and booklets for many kinds of construction equipment, including cranes, crawler tractors, loader/dozers, off-highway trucks, graders, scrapers, excavators, and compactors.

Finally, equipment manufacturers often sell safety devices for their equipment and supply safety manuals for each piece of equipment. At least one manufacturer, Caterpillar Tractor Co., loans and sells 16-millimeter safety films to the public.

Equipment dealers may also have films, slides, posters, and similar safety promotional material, plus safety manuals for individual pieces of equipment. Addresses for the sources listed above are included at the end of this chapter.

SAFETY PRECAUTIONS

As mentioned previously, safety programs must be tailored to fit the needs of individual contractors and their operations. Accordingly, to supplement the foregoing general listing of safety program preliminaries, the following sample of specific safety precautions is presented, some of which are condensed from safety publications of the Power Crane and Shovel Association:

1. Thoroughly inspect any machine before starting it. Check fuel, lubricants, hydraulic levels, and the like. Look for damage, hydraulic leaks, etc.

2. Keep machines clean, including windows and foot pedals. Remove grease, mud, etc., from both shoes before starting any machine.

3. Avoid wearing loose clothing, jewelry, and other items that might get caught on or in a machine.

4. Wear protective clothing—hard hat, safety glasses and shoes, etc.—as appropriate.

5. Be sure that machines are equipped with appropriate safety equipment, e.g., protective panels, rollover protective structures (ROPs), fire extinguishers, first aid kits, etc.

6. Check height, width, and weight restrictions in the area of operation. Make sure that the equipment does not exceed the stated or implied limitations.

7. Think about possible hazards and plan ahead for them. Be prepared to act quickly in case of accidents, fire, etc.

8. Provide for good machine visibility by removing vandal guards and other obstructions. Poor visibility can cause accidents.

9. Know exactly where potential hazards such as power lines are located. Know your working area thoroughly and take appropriate precautions.

10. Know the load ratings of machines and never exceed them.

11. Know the communications system that will be used. ANSI has established nationally recognized hand signals. Whatever the system used, the operators and the designated signal person should discuss and agree on it before any machines are operated.

12. Watch for slippery surfaces when mounting machinery. Use the proper grab bars.

13. Check all controls to be sure that they are in the correct position according to the manufacturer's manual before starting the engine.

14. Check for warning tags. (Warning tags are used to call attention to problems.) These tags, usually placed at the starting switch or near some other controls, should not be removed except by the person who installed them or by someone who is otherwise aware of the circumstances to which the tags apply.

15. Do not start or attempt to operate equipment except from an approved operator station. (Do not reach in through the cab window to start the engine from outside, etc.)

16. Provide adequate ventilation and/or protection from exhaust fumes.

17. Keep all machine tools, parts, containers, etc., in their proper place, not in places where they may interfere with the machine or otherwise create problems.

18. Avoid touching any machine with bare skin in extreme cold; skin can freeze to the metal.

19. Do not eat or drink while operating a machine.

20. Do not operate a machine while under the influence of medication or drugs. Similarly, do not operate a machine when overly fatigued. (Take appropriate work breaks, get rest, etc.)

21. Watch out for people near any operating machine. Do not allow workers under the crane boom, do not allow them to ride the hook or load, etc.

22. Set and lock all brakes, engage all ratchets, etc., when holding a load.

23. Be aware of and use appropriate manufacturer safety devices such as rollover protective structures (ROPs), warning horns, back-up alarms, rear view mirrors, and sound suppressors. Many of these devices can actually increase productivity and cut down on manpower requirements.

24. Follow the manufacturer's instructions for maintaining equipment, refueling, adding hydraulic fluid, etc.

25. Always think safety; it saves lives, pain, and money.

No safety program or list of rules can assure worker safety. Rather, the most important aspects of a safety program are to (1) educate workers about proper safety procedures, and (2) make safety a key ingredient in all construction activities, keeping it in the minds of all involved, from top management to individual workers.

SOURCES OF SAFETY INFORMATION

CIMA has operator safety manuals for heavy equipment, safety education slide programs, safety posters and decals, and technical bulletins and standards. Catalogs, order forms, and price lists are available from

Construction Industry Manufacturers Association
111 East Wisconsin Avenue
Milwaukee, Wisconsin 53202-4879

Caterpillar Tractor Co. has safety films, too. Write:

Caterpillar Tractor Co.
Advertising Department
Peoria, Illinois 61629

Other sources of safety information and standards include:

The American National Standards Institute (ANSI)

The Society of Automotive Engineers (SAE)

The Occupational Safety and Health Administration (OSHA)

The Mine Safety and Health Administration (MSHA)

12

PRODUCTION
ESTIMATION

The initial purpose of production estimation is usually to arrive at an accurate bid figure; thus, good production estimation can mean the difference between getting a job and not getting it. If the job is gotten and goes into production, actual progress reports are used to spotlight problems and update production estimation. Finally, of course, the contractor's predicted profit is dependent on how good the initial production estimate was.

Important as production estimation is, it is essentially a simple arithmetic process. But there are many variables involved and many details to consider which tend to make it a tedious process. For example, there are many different pieces and brands of construction equipment, each with its own functions and capabilities. Then there are such variables as site conditions, materials to be handled, operator experience and efficiency, and age and condition of equipment. And then, to further complicate the process, an estimator will frequently be asked to determine if and when new equipment will be purchased and the effect of those purchases on existing and future jobs—all with an eye on the contractor's particular business situation.

Thus, the estimator will often be poring over manufacturers' literature and equipment specifications, trying to determine the most profitable course to take. Of course, there will always be many variables to consider in arriving at the best decision; but regardless of the number of variables, there are certain engineering factors the estimator must be familiar with in order to understand the claims of manufacturers' specifications. Accordingly, it is appropriate to begin a study of production estimation with some commonly used engineering terms, definitions, and methods.

ENGINEERING FACTORS

The following factors are frequently encountered in equipment specifications and data, and production estimation calculations:

1. Rolling resistance
2. Grade resistance and grade assistance
3. Rimpull and drawbar pull
4. Rimpull required
5. Available rimpull
6. Usable rimpull
7. Travel speed
8. Cycle time
9. Trips per hour
10. Bank yards, loose yards, and compacted yards

11. Efficiency and production per working hour

12. Altitude deration

13. Owning and operating costs

14. Cost per cubic yard

15. Cost per compacted cubic yard

16. Loader production

17. Motor grader production

These factors are discussed in the following text.

Rolling Resistance

Rolling resistance may be defined as a combination of forces that retard or oppose the movement of a wheel over level terrain. Rubber-tired tractors and other self-propelled wheel units, as well as trailers, scrapers, and other towed, wheeled vehicles are typical vehicles affected by rolling resistance. Rolling resistance is caused mainly by the penetration of the tire into the surface terrain and by the flexing of the tire itself. It is one of the items that must be considered when selecting the type and power of the vehicle needed for a particular project.

The value of rolling resistance for a given type of surface may be expressed in pounds per ton of vehicle weight. Table 12–1 lists five typical surfaces encountered in construction work, with their corresponding rolling resistance factors. Surfaces falling in between those shown may have their rolling resistance factors arrived at by interpolation.

Table 12–1. Typical rolling resistance factors.

ROAD CONDITION	RESISTANCE VALUES IN LB/TON
Hard, smooth, stabilized surface with no tire penetration (such as a well-maintained concrete or blacktop road).	40
Firm, smooth surface, flexing slightly under load (such as a gravel road).	65
Irregular dirt surface, flexing considerably under load (such as a rutted dirt road where the tires penetrate about one inch).	100
Soft dirt surface, not stabilized, irregular (such as a rough dirt roadway where the tires penetrate about 4 inches).	150
Soft, muddy surface (such as a muddy or sandy roadway where the tires penetrate 6 inches or more).	200 to 400

Rolling resistance for a particular vehicle over a given surface may be arrived at by the following formula:

$$RR = \text{rolling resistance (lb)} = \text{weight on wheels (tons)} \times \text{rolling resistance factor (lb/ton)}$$

Thus, RR for a 4,000-pound automobile on a level concrete surface would be 2 tons × 40 lb/ton = 80 lb. That is, the automobile must overcome 80 pounds of rolling resistance before it can move. Similarly, a wheeled tractor–scraper weighing 66,000 pounds and carrying a 48,000-pound load on a flexible dirt roadway must overcome 5,700 pounds of rolling resistance (57 tons × 100 lb/ton) before it can move.

Grade Resistance and Grade Assistance

Rolling resistance is measured for level terrain. Obviously, no vehicle will always be on level terrain; thus, the effect of the grade must be added to rolling resistance to determine the total resistance on a vehicle. There are two possibilities: *grade resistance* is the retarding force that must be overcome to move a vehicle uphill; *grade assistance* is the force that helps the vehicle move downhill. In both cases, gravity is the force in question.

Grades are measured in percent of slope in earthmoving work. For example, if a vehicle must travel up 5 feet for every 20 feet it travels horizontally, the vehicle is negotiating a 25% grade (5/20 = .25 = 25%). Since uphill grades are called *adverse*, the vehicle would be traveling a 25% adverse grade.

It has been found that for each 1 percent of grade, a force of 20 pounds per ton of vehicle gross weight is produced. This force is hindering for adverse grades and helping for downhill grades (called *favorable* grades). The formula for grade resistance is

$$GR = \text{grade resistance} = \text{total weight (tons)} \times 20 \text{ lb/ton} \times \text{percent grade}$$

Consequently, if a loaded vehicle weighing 60 tons must travel up a 5% adverse grade, the grade resistance would be

$$60 \text{ tons} \times 20 \text{ lb/ton} \times 5 = 6,000 \text{ lb}$$

Grade assistance is figured in exactly the same way as grade resistance, but the results assist the vehicle rather than hinder it. In the example given, if the grade were 5% favorable, and if all the other factors were the same, we would have 6,000 pounds of grade *assistance* in moving the vehicle down the hill.

In general,

$$\text{Total resistance} = \text{rolling resistance} + \text{grade resistance}$$
$$(\text{or grade assistance})$$

Rimpull and Drawbar Pull

Rubber-tired vehicles such as tractors, trucks, and other self-propelled vehicles depend on the contact of the wheels with the ground or terrain for their motion. *Rimpull* is the term used to describe the pushing force exerted by the tire against the terrain surface. Rimpull is expressed in pounds.

Unlike the rubber-tired vehicles, crawler tractors carry their travel surface with them in the form of their tracks. *Drawbar pull,* the crawler tractor counterpart of rimpull, is the amount of pull power at the drawbar after horsepower losses have been subtracted due to friction in the gear trains, differential, etc. Both drawbar pull and rimpull vary inversely with tractor unit speed. That is, power is greatest but speed is low in the lower gears, whereas speed is greatest but power is low in the high gears. Manufacturers typically provide graphs or other information giving maximum speeds and power for each gear. (See Figure 12–1.)

Rimpull Required and Available Rimpull

Rimpull required is the amount of rimpull needed to overcome the effects of rolling resistance and grade resistance—that is, the rimpull required to overcome the total resistance. (Recall that total resistance = rolling resistance + grade resistance (or grade assistance).

Available Rimpull is the amount of force available between the drive tires and the ground. Manufacturers sometimes give the available rimpull for each gear of the machine. If a case occurs in which one does not, the following formula may be used for an approximation:

$$\text{Available rimpull} = \frac{\text{engine horsepower} \times 375 \times \text{efficiency of gear train}}{\text{miles per hour}}$$

In the formula, 375 is a constant. The efficiency of various machines depends largely on the type of gear train they have, as well as the type of transmission they use. Generally speaking, the efficiency of the gear train ranges between 70 and 85%. If it is unknown, the efficiency may be assumed to be 85%.

As an example, let us find the available rimpull of a wheeled tractor–scraper traveling in sixth gear at 13 miles per hour. The horsepower is 450, but the manufacturer does not list the efficiency of the gear train. Using the above formula, we have

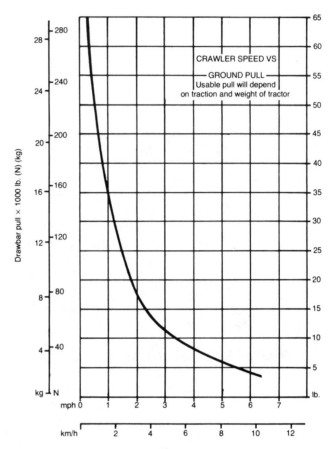

Figure 12–1. Drawbar pull vs. speed for John Deere 850 crawler tractor. Maximum drawbar pull is 65,000 lb at 0.20 mph.

$$\text{Available rimpull} = \frac{450 \text{ horsepower} \times 375 \text{ (constant)} \times 85\% \text{ (efficiency)}}{13 \text{ mph}}$$

$$= 11,034 \text{ lb}$$

It is important to note that available rimpull is the amount of force available where the tire touches the ground, *without figuring in the wheel slippage*. Therefore, not all the actual force available at the tire will actually be usable.

Usable Rimpull

Usable rimpull takes slippage of the wheels into account and is therefore the actual amount of pull or push that the wheels can deliver at their point of contact with the ground. Like available rimpull, usable rimpull is expressed in pounds; however, unlike available rimpull, it does not consider engine horsepower in its determination. Usable Rimpull may be found by the formula

Usable rimpull = traction factor × weight on drive wheels (pounds)

Traction factors have been worked out for most of the ground conditions encountered in construction work. (See Table 12–2.)

As an application of the formula, the usable rimpull for an off-highway truck with a loaded weight of 130,000 pounds on the drive wheels traveling over a loose gravel road is 130,000 lb × .36 = 46,800 lb. Manufacturers usually supply distribution figures for loads on their vehicles, e.g., the weight on the front and rear tires when loaded and when empty. Accordingly, it is not difficult to determine, with reasonable accuracy, how much weight is on each of the vehicle's wheels both when the vehicle is loaded and when it is empty.

Always use the lesser of available rimpull and usable rimpull in production estimating calculations.

Travel Speed

Travel speed is the speed at which a vehicle can travel in its various gears. Normally, the manufacturer provides travel speed data under certain conditions. When rolling resistance, grade resistance or assistance, rimpull required, and available and usable rimpull are computed, precise travel speeds may then be determined.

Cycle Time

Cycle time is the amount of time it takes a machine to complete one circuit of its operations. Cycle time is composed of (1) fixed time, and (2) variable time, also called travel time.

Table 12–2. Traction factors for rubber tires on typical surfaces.

SURFACE	TRACTION FACTOR—RUBBER TIRES
Concrete	.90
Clay Loam, Dry	.55
Clay Loam, Wet	.45
Rutted Clay Loam	.40
Loose Sand	.30
Quarry Pit	.65
Gravel Road (loose)	.36
Packed Snow	.20
Ice	.12
Firm Earth	.55
Loose Earth	.45
Coal, Stockpiled	.45

Source: John Deere Company

Table 12–3. Typical fixed-time constants.

WHEELED TRACTOR/SCRAPER COMBINATIONS	BASIC FIXED TIME CONSTANTS FOR—		
	4TH GEAR RANGE	3D GEAR RANGE	2D GEAR RANGE
Loading (with pushers)	.7 min	.7 min	.7 min
Dumping and turning	.6 min	.6 min	.6 min
Acceleration and deceleration ...	.9 min	.7 min	.4 min
Total fixed time	2.2 min	2.0 min	1.7 min
Crawler dozers (shuttle dozing only):	Using the same transmission, shifting only with forward–reverse lever.	With the transmission shifted to higher gear when going in reverse.	
Total fixed time—one cycle	0.10 min	0.20 min	
Crawler tractor/scraper combinations.	Self-loading	Push-loaded	
Loading	1.5 min	1.0 min	
Dumping and turning	1.0 min	1.0 min	
Total fixed time	2.5 min	2.0 min	

Source: U.S. Army

Fixed time is that time used by a machine for purposes other than hauling and returning. Loading, turning, and dumping, for instance, are fixed-time operations. They are called fixed-time operations because the time it takes to do them is about the same regardless of the haul and return distance, the condition of the haul road, etc. For example, it takes the same time to dump a load of gravel regardless of whether you haul it 300 feet or 300 miles. Table 12–3 shows some standard fixed-time constants. Fixed-time constants for specific pieces of equipment can usually be obtained from the manufacturer.

Variable time, or travel time, is the time actually spent on the haul road moving material and returning for more. Variable time may be found by the formula

$$\text{Variable time} = \frac{\text{haul distance in feet}}{(\text{speed in miles per hour}) \times (88 \text{ ft per min})}$$

Note that the formula will automatically convert speeds in miles per hour to speeds in feet per minute. This is done because haul distances are always kept to the minimum, so that feet per minute is appropriate.

Trips Per Hour

Once cycle time is known, it is convenient to compute the number of cycles possible per hour. The following formula is used:

$$\text{Trips/hour} = \frac{\text{minutes/hour}}{\text{cycle time (in minutes)/trip}}$$

A 5-minute cycle, for example, would yield

$$\frac{60 \text{ minutes/hour}}{5 \text{ minutes/trip}} = 12 \text{ trips/hour}$$

Bank Yards, Loose Yards, and Compacted Yards

Earthmoving typically involves the excavation, hauling, and compacting of earth. In its natural or undisturbed state, earth is measured in *bank yards*. When it is removed from the natural state, it swells, or increases in volume, due to the creation of tiny voids. It is then measured in *loose yards*. Typically, the loose earth is then compacted in the fill location so that it becomes even more tightly packed than it was in its bank or natural state. This is done to prepare the earth for loads that will be placed on it—buildings, roadways, parking lots, etc. Compacted earth is measured in *compacted yards*.

A typical comparison of the three measures is shown in Figure 12–2 and Table 12–4.

Construction equipment has both volume and weight handling limitations. Thus, it is necessary to understand the relationship between the above three types of measure to properly select equipment and to estimate its production.

The weights of common materials encountered in earthmoving are well documented. Many weight tables such as Table 12–5 are available to speed calculations.

The percent that a material swells (% swell) affects the handling of the material. This increase in the percent volume of the material may be determined by the formula

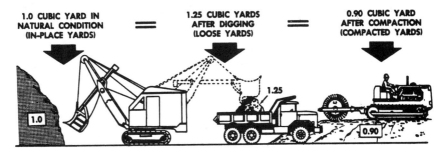

Figure 12–2. Volume change in loam caused by handling. Source: U.S. Army.

Table 12–4. *Soil volume conversion factors.*

SOIL TYPE	SOIL CONDITION INITIALLY	BANK (IN-PLACE)	CONVERTED TO LOOSE	CONVERTED TO COMPACTED
Sand	Bank (In-Place)	- - - -	1.11	0.95
	Loose	.90	- - - -	.86
	Compacted	1.05	1.17	- - - -
Loam	Bank (In-Place)	- - - -	1.25	0.90
	Loose	.80	- - - -	.72
	Compacted	1.11	1.39	- - - -
Clay	Bank (In-Place)	- - - -	1.43	0.90
	Loose	.70	- - - -	.63
	Compacted	1.11	1.59	- - - -
Rock (blasted)	Bank (In-Place)	- - - -	1.50	1.30
	Loose	.67	- - - -	.87
	Compacted	.77	1.15	- - - -
Coral comparable to limestone	Bank (In-Place)	- - - -	1.50	1.30
	Loose	.67	- - - -	.87
	Compacted	.77	1.15	- - - -

Source: U.S. Army

Table 12–5. *Approximate weights of materials. Typical weights for common materials are well known and help speed production estimation calculations. Where more precise calculations are required, approximate weights must be adjusted for variations in compaction, moisture content, and other factors that may influence weight.*

MATERIAL	POUNDS PER YARD^3 BANK	POUNDS PER YARD^3 LOOSE
Caliche	3,700	2,100
Cinders	1,450	1,000
Clay, natural bed	2,900	2,100
Clay, dry	2,700	2,000
Clay, wet	3,200	2,500
Clay and gravel, dry	2,800	2,200
Clay and gravel, wet	3,200	2,600
Coal, anthracite, natural bed	2,500	1,800
Coal, bituminous, natural bed	2,200	1,600
Earth, dry loam	2,600	2,100
Earth, moist loam	3,200	2,560
Granite, broken	4,500	2,800
Gravel, dry	3,100	2,800
Gravel, wet	3,700	3,300
Gravel, pit run, sandy	3,600	3,200
Kaolin	2,800	2,160
Limestone, broken	4,200	2,600
Sand, dry	2,700	2,400
Sand, moist	3,300	2,900
Sand, wet	3,500	3,100
Sandstone	4,100	2,600
Sand with gravel, dry	3,250	2,900
Sand with gravel, wet	3,800	3,400
Topsoil	2,300	1,600
Shale	3,500	2,500

Source: John Deere

$$\% \text{ swell} = \frac{\text{bank weight in pounds/cubic yard}}{\text{loose weight in pounds/cubic yard}}$$

The ratio between loose measure and bank measure is called the *load factor,* which may be found by the formula

$$\text{Load factor} = \frac{\text{loose weight in pounds/cubic yard}}{\text{bank weight in pounds/cubic yard}}$$

If % Swell is known, the load factor may be found as follows:

$$\text{Load factor} = \frac{100}{100 + \% \text{ swell}}$$

Similarly, if the load factor is known, % swell may be found by means of the formula

$$\% \text{Swell} = \left(\frac{1}{\text{Load Factor}} - 1 \right) \times 100$$

Load factor and % swell tables are readily available. (See Table 12–6.)

Table 12–6. Load factor and % swell tables are readily available for many materials.
Source:

MATERIAL	LOAD FACTOR	% SWELL
Caliche	.57	76
Cinders	.69	45
Clay, natural bed	.72	38
Clay, dry	.74	35
Clay, wet	.78	28
Clay and gravel, dry	.79	27
Clay and gravel, wet	.81	23
Coal, anthracite, natural bed	.72	39
Coal, bituminous, natural bed	.73	38
Earth, dry loam	.81	24
Earth, moist loam	.80	25
Granite, broken	.62	61
Gravel, dry	.90	11
Gravel, wet	.89	12
Gravel, pit run, sandy	.89	13
Kaolin	.77	30
Limestone, broken	.62	62
Sand, dry	.89	13
Sand, moist	.88	14
Sand, wet	.89	13
Sandstone	.63	58
Sand with gravel, dry	.89	12
Sand with gravel, wet	.89	12
Topsoil	.70	44
Shale	.71	40

Source: John Deere

Different jobs require different compactions, and these compaction requirements should be spelled out in the job specifications, usually by the project engineer. Compaction, which is a reduction in volume of earth, is referred to as *shrinkage* in earthmoving calculations. The *shrinkage factor* may be found as follows:

$$\text{Shrinkage factor} = \frac{\text{compacted cubic yards}}{\text{bank cubic yards}}$$

A little algebraic manipulation yields

$$\text{Bank cubic yards} = \frac{\text{compacted cubic yards}}{\text{shrinkage factor}}$$

and

$$\text{Compacted cubic yards} = \text{bank cubic yards} \times \text{shrinkage factor}$$

Finally, the following formulas may be derived from some of those given earlier:

$$\text{Bank cubic yards} = \text{loose cubic yards} \times \text{load factor}$$

$$\text{Loose cubic yards} = \frac{\text{bank cubic yards}}{\text{load factor}}$$

$$= \text{bank cubic yards} \times \frac{100 + \% \text{ swell}}{100}$$

All these formulas help define the relationship between earth in its three states: bank (natural), loose (in the haul unit), and compacted (in use at the fill site). The contractor is often called on to handle earth in all three of these conditions, and these simple formulas aid in figuring equipment needs and production capabilities.

The following examples illustrate the application of some of the formulas:

Example

A haul unit is carrying 10 bank cubic yards of natural bed clay per load. How many loose yards is the haul unit carrying? How many compacted yards will be available per load if the shrinkage factor is .80?

Solution:

$$\text{Loose yards} = (\text{bank yards}) \left(\frac{100 + \% \text{ swell}}{100} \right) = 10 \left(\frac{100 + 38}{100} \right)$$

$$= 10 \times 1.38 = 13.8 \approx 14 \text{ cubic yards}$$

$$\text{Compacted cubic yards} = \text{bank yards} \times \text{shrinkage factor}$$
$$= 10 \times .80 = 8 \text{ cubic yards}$$

In other words, 10 bank yards were dug out, which swelled to 14 loose yards in the truck or haul unit, and which will be compacted to 8 compacted yards when the earth is in use at the site.

Example   What is the load factor of a material which has a loose weight of 2,400 pounds/cubic yard and a bank weight of 2,700 pounds/cubic yard?

Solution:

$$\text{Load factor} = \frac{\text{loose weight in pounds/cubic yard}}{\text{bank weight in pounds/cubic yard}}$$

$$= \frac{2,400 \text{ pounds/cubic yard}}{2,700 \text{ pounds/cubic yard}} = .89$$

Example   If a scraper is heaped with 12 cubic yards of dry loam earth, how many bank yards are being carried?

Solution: $\text{Bank yards} = \text{loose yards} \times \text{load factor} = 12 \times .81 = 9.72 \approx 10$

Example   A material weighs 3,200 pounds bank and 2,100 pounds loose. What is the % swell?

Solution:

$$\% \text{ Swell} = \frac{\text{bank weight in pounds/cubic yard}}{\text{loose weight in pounds/cubic yard}}$$

$$= \frac{3,200 \text{ pounds/cubic yard}}{2,100 \text{ pounds/cubic yard}} \approx 52\%$$

Efficiency and Production Per Working Hour

Maximum production for a given unit of equipment is rarely, if ever, possible, because of normal operator inefficiencies, break times, weather and terrain difficulties, and numerous other factors. Thus, it becomes necessary to apply a factor less than 100% to hourly production. Once the job is under way, very accurate efficiency factors may be obtained. For initial estimating purposes, the following efficiency factors have been shown to be reasonably accurate:

		WORKING HOUR	EFFICIENCY FACTOR
Day	Crawler	50 min/hour	.83
	Wheel	45 min/hour	.75
Night	Crawler	45 min/hour	.75
	Wheel	40 min/hour	.67

These efficiency factors are nothing more than percentages of an hour. The exact factor chosen would be a matter of judgment based on field conditions.

Example

Suppose a machine is physically capable of making 15 cycles an hour in hauling 14 bank yards. If the unit is a wheel tractor that is operating at night, how many bank yards will the machine produce under actual field conditions?

Solution

(15 cycles/hour × 14 bank yards) × (.67 efficiency factor) = 140.7 ≈ 141 bank yards per hour

Altitude Deration

As construction equipment is moved higher in elevation, the reduced atmosphere causes a reduction in engine horsepower. Thus, the manufacturer's rated drawbar pull or rimpull must be *derated*, or reduced, in production estimating calculations.

For elevations up to about 3,000 feet, there is little, if any, loss of power. Above 3,000 feet, rough estimates of deration may be found by adding 3% loss of power for each 1,000 feet higher that the equipment is moved (unless the engine is turbocharged or supercharged, in which case adding the 3% loss of power for each 1,000 feet doesn't generally begin until 5,000 feet in elevation is reached).

More accurate deration estimates may be obtained by consulting manufacturer deration tables.

Owning and Operating Costs

Construction equipment costs must be considered relative to the particular user's operation. Since there can be many variations, it is difficult (and dangerous) to generalize about cost computations. However, equipment costs for all users will fall into two broad categories: owning costs and operating costs. The following terms and definitions are basic to a study of equipment costs.

Owning Costs are costs associated with simply owning the machinery, whether or not it is operated. Owning costs typically include:

1. Depreciation

2. Interest, insurance, and storage

3. Taxes, licenses, and freight

The machine will incur such costs even if it is parked in a garage.

Operating costs are those costs directly related to the operation of the equipment. Typically, they include the following:

1. Fuel

2. Servicing costs

3. Repair costs and the repair reserve

4. Tires

5. Special-wear items

6. Operator hourly wages (usually added in last)

A more detailed explanation of these terms follows.

Depreciation. There are two kinds of depreciation: (1) loss of value due to physical deterioration of the equipment and/or improvements in later models, and (2) losses shown as an accounting deduction related to applicable current tax laws.

The first kind of depreciation is typically brought about by normal wear and tear on the machine due to actual field use, weather or other natural elements, age, etc. Manufacturers often supply figures for the average life of their equipment. Caterpillar, for example, breaks the work done into three ''zones'' of difficulty, from relatively easy conditions to very difficult ones, and estimates the life span of the equipment accordingly. (See Table 12–7.)

Depreciation for tax purposes is not nearly as straightforward as the first kind of depreciation. Moreover, a contractor's tax position can alter the way he or she does business. Therefore, it is best to work in consultation with qualified accountants who are experienced in construction accounting when handling depreciation for tax purposes. Briefly, this kind of depreciation is usually figured using one of the following methods:

1. Straight line

2. Sum of the digits

3. Double declining balance

Straight line   With the straight-line method, the amount to be depreciated is applied evenly over the life of the equipment.

Table 12–7. Caterpillar has evolved a quick estimator guide for equipment life under various work conditions. It is, however, only a guide and may change with modifications to the equipment.

	ZONE A	ZONE B	ZONE C
0–10 **TRACK-TYPE** **TRACTORS**	Pulling scrapers, most agricultural drawbar, stockpile, coalpile and landfill work. No impact. Intermittent full throttle operation.	Production dozing in clays, sands, gravels. Pushloading scrapers, borrow pit ripping, most landclearing and skidding applications. Medium impact conditions.	Heavy rock ripping. Tandem ripping. Pushloading and dozing in hard rock. Work on rock surfaces. Continuous high impact conditions.
D3–D7 **D8–10**	12,000 Hr 22,000 Hr	10,000 Hr 18,000 Hr	8,000 Hr 15,000 Hr
12–20 **MOTOR GRADERS**	Light road maintenance. Finishing. Plant and road mix work. Light snowplowing. Large amounts of traveling.	Haul road maintenance. Road construction, ditching. Loose fill spreading. Landforming, landleveling. Summer road maintenance with medium to heavy winter snow removal. Elevating grader use.	Maintenance of hard packed roads with embedded rock. Heavy fill spreading. Ripping-scarifying of asphalt or concrete. Continuous high load factor. High impact.
	10,000 Hr	15,000 Hr	12,000 Hr
200 **EXCAVATORS**	Shallow depth utility construction where excavator sets pipe and digs only 3 or 4 hours/shift. Free flowing, low density material and little or no impact. Most scrap handling arrangements.	Mass excavation or trenching where machine digs all the time in natural bed clay soils. Some traveling and steady, full throttle operation. Most log loading applications.	Continuous trenching or truck loading in rock or shot rock soils. Large amount of travel over rough ground. Machine continuously working on rock floor with constant high load factor and high impact.
	12,000 Hr	10,000 Hr	8,000 Hr
200 **FRONT SHOVELS**	Continuous loading in loose banks or stockpile. Good underfoot conditions. (Might be considered similar to "normal" wheel loader conditions.)	Continuous loading in well-shot rock or fairly tight bank. Good underfoot conditions; dry floor, little impact or sliding or undercarriage.	Continuous loading in poorly-shot rock, virgin or lightly-blasted tight banks, e.g., shales, cemented gravels, caliches etc. Adverse underfoot conditions: rough floors; high impact sliding on under carriage.
	18,000 Hr	15,000 Hr	10,000 Hr
200 **LOGGER**	Continuous felling and stacking in good underfoot conditions. Little travel.	Continuous cycling in good underfoot conditions. Some traveling and steady, full throttle operation.	Continuous full throttle cycling. Some travel over stumpy terrain. High load factor on sloping underfoot conditions.
	18,000 Hr	15,000 Hr	10,000 Hr

Table 12–7. (Continued) Caterpillar has evolved a quick estimator guide for equipment life under various work conditions. It is, however, only a guide and may change with modifications to the equipment.

	ZONE A	ZONE B	ZONE C
500 **WHEEL SKIDDERS**	Intermittent skidding for short distances, no decking. Good underfoot conditions: level terrain, dry floor, few if any stumps. 12,000 Hr	Continuous turning, steady skidding for medium distances with moderate decking. Good underfooting: dry floor with few stumps and gradual rolling terrain. 10,000 Hr	Continuous turning, steady skidding for long distances with frequent decking. Poor underfoot conditions: wet floor, steep slopes and numerous stumps. 8,000 Hr
550 **PIPELAYERS**	Little or no use in mud, water or on rock. Use on level, regular surfaces. 15,000 Hr	Typical pipelayer use in operating conditions ranging from very good to severe. 13,000 Hr	Continuous use in deep mud or water or on rock surfaces. 10,000 Hr
600 **WHEEL TRACTOR SCRAPERS**	Level or favorable hauls on good haul roads. No impact. Easy-loading materials.	Varying loading and haul road conditions. Long and short hauls. Adverse and favorable grades. Some impact. Typical road-building use on a variety of jobs.	High impact condition, such as loading ripped rock. Overloading. Continuous high total resistance conditions. Rough haul roads.
613B, 615 **All others**	12,000 Hr 16,000 Hr	10,000 Hr 12,000 Hr	8,000 Hr 8,000 Hr
700 **OFF HIGHWAY TRUCKS & TRACTORS**	Mine and quarry use with properly matched loading equipment. Well maintained haul roads. Also construction use under above conditions. 25,000 Hr	Varying loading and haul road conditions. Long and short hauls. Adverse and favorable grades. Some impact. Typical road-building use on a variety of jobs. 20,000 Hr	Consistently poor haul road conditions. Extreme overloading. Oversized loading equipment. 15,000 Hr
800 **WHEEL TRACTORS & COMPACTORS**	Light utility work. Stockpile work. Pulling compactors. Dozing loose fill. No impact. 15,000 Hr	Production dozing, push-loading in clays, sands, silts, loose gravels. Shovel clean-up. Compactor use. 12,000 Hr	Production dozing in rock. Pushloading in rocky, bouldery borrow pits. High impact conditions. 8,000 Hr

(Continued on next page)

185

Table 12–7. (Continued) Caterpillar has evolved a quick estimator guide for equipment life under various work conditions. It is, however, only a guide and may change with modifications to the equipment.

	ZONE A	ZONE B	ZONE C
900 **WHEEL LOADERS**	Intermittent truck loading from stockpile, hopper charging on firm, smooth surfaces. Free flowing, low density materials. Utility work in governmental and industrial applications. Light snowplowing. Load and carry on good surface for short distances with no grades.	Continuous truck loading from stockpile. Low to medium density materials in properly sized bucket. Hopper charging in low to medium rolling resistance. Loading from bank in good digging. Load and carry on poor surfaces and slight adverse grades.	Loading shot rock (large loaders). Handling high density materials with counterweighted machine. Steady loading from very tight banks. Continuous work on rough or very soft surfaces. Load and carry in hard digging; travel longer distances on poor surfaces with adverse grades.
910–966	12,000 Hr	10,000 Hr	8,000 Hr
980–992	15,000 Hr	12,000 Hr	10,000 Hr
900 **TRACK-TYPE** **LOADERS**	Intermittent truck loading from stockpile. Minimum traveling, turning. Free flowing, low density materials with standard bucket. No impact.	Bank excavation, intermittent ripping, basement digging of natural bed clays, sands, silts, gravels. Some traveling. Steady full throttle operation.	Loading shot rock, cobbles, glacial till, caliche. Steel mill work. High density materials in standard bucket. Continuous work on rock surfaces. Large amount of ripping of tight, rocky materials. High impact conditions.
	12,000 Hr	10,000 Hr	8,000 Hr

Source: Caterpillar Tractor Company

Example

Compute the annual depreciation by the straight-line method for a diesel-powered $160,000 wheel loader working under difficult circumstances, namely, loading rock and other heavy materials continuously on rocky surfaces and in cramped quarters, and then traveling a considerable distance on deep, muddy roads with adverse grades before unloading. The manufacturer estimates a four-year depreciation period for these operating conditions, which is less than the period normally allowed by the IRS for this piece of equipment. The accountant decides that the lesser period is defensible.

Local equipment auction prices and past sales experience of the equipment owner indicate that the salvage value of the equipment is $22,000. Annual depreciation is computed with the following formula:

$$\text{Annual depreciation} = \frac{\text{cost} - \text{salvage*}}{\text{life (in years)}}$$

Solution:

$$\text{Depreciation} = \frac{160,000 - 22,000}{4} = \$34,500/\text{year}$$

Sum of the
digits

      The sum-of-the-digits method recognizes the fact that there is greater decline in the value of a machine during the first year than the second, greater during the second than the third year, etc. The total amount of depreciation taken is the same, but the amount per year varies. The formula for depreciation for a particular year using this method is

$$D_n = \frac{\text{year digit}}{\text{sum of digits}} \times \text{ amount to be depreciated}$$

where D_n is the depreciation in year n; year digit is the year to be computed, but in inverse order; and sum of digits is the sum of the year numbers (1, 2, 3, . . .) for the period to be depreciated.

Example

      Using the same problem as in the straight-line example, we see that the sum of the digits for the four-year period to be depreciated is $1 + 2 + 3 + 4 = 10$. Therefore, depreciation for each of the four years is:

$$D_1 = 4/10 \times (160,000 - 22,000) = 55,200$$
$$D_2 = 3/10 \times 138,000 = 41,400$$
$$D_3 = 2/10 \times 138,000 = 27,600$$
$$D_4 = 1/10 \times 138,000 = 13,800$$

Double
declining
balance

      In the double-declining-balance method, the annual depreciation for a particular year is found using the formula

$$D_n = \frac{200\%}{n} \times \text{book value at beginning of year}$$

where n equals the equipment life, or depreciation period, in years. Note that although salvage life is not subtracted from book value in the formula, book value may never go below salvage value.

*The cost of tires, normally an operating cost, may be subtracted from salvage value under allowable circumstances.

Example   Using the same wheel loader as in the previous examples, we have

$$D_n = \frac{200\%}{4} \times \text{book value at beginning of year,}$$

so that

$$D_1 = .50 \times 160,000 = 80,000$$
$$D_2 = .50 \times (160,000 - 80,000) = 40,000$$
$$D_3 = .50 \times (80,000 - 40,000) = 20,000$$

However, in D_3 we note that $20,000 is less than the salvage value, $22,000. Thus, we may claim only $18,000 that year (80,000 + 40,000 + 18,000 = 138,000 = initial book value − salvage value.) Further, no depreciation may be claimed the fourth year.

The reader should note that the exact method chosen for depreciating equipment depends on both current tax laws and the particular operations and needs of individual equipment users.

Interest, Insurance, and Storage. Typically, equipment users borrow money from lending institutions and/or investors for purchasing equipment. They also invest some of their own money (equity) in the equipment. The interest on such loans is a cost to the user. The user, of course, expects to increase productivity and profits with the equipment and thereby more than offset such costs.

Insurance is necessary to cover equipment-related damages. Insurance premiums are a cost.

Construction equipment is expensive and must be protected with adequate storage facilities. Storage costs may include those for

1. Storage facilities and/or covers, fences, tarpaulins, etc.
2. Machine tie-downs and blockings on trucks
3. Periodic maintenance
4. Wages for watchmen and associated storage personnel
5. Other purchases related to storage

Taxes, Licenses, and Freight. Costs for taxes, licenses, and freight include those for

1. Personal property and sales taxes
2. Licenses for operating vehicles on public roads and related expenses

3. Freight transportation from the manufacturer's plant to the desired user location and associated expenses related to getting the machine in operation

Fuel. Fuel is an operating cost. Fuel consumption varies widely, depending mostly on the level of difficulty of the work and the driving habits of the operator. That is, difficult materials and working conditions that require full power continuously or for long periods result in higher fuel consumption than easier materials with less power requirements. Similarly, different operators, using different operating techniques and/or possessing different working temperaments and attitudes, can result in a variation of over 10% in fuel consumption—just as different drivers of the same automobile will get different gas mileages.

Equipment manufacturers often provide estimation tables for fuel consumption under various power requirements. However, each machine will have a different fuel consumption rate, and each will typically be used for various tasks on the job, thereby complicating the estimates. Thus, all tables, formulas, and other estimating tools must be used with detailed field conditions in mind whenever possible.

The formula for estimating fuel cost, once the hourly consumption has been estimated as accurately as possible, is a simple one, namely,

Hourly fuel costs = hourly consumption $\times$ local unit price of fuel

Servicing costs. Servicing costs include those for lubrication oils and grease, hydraulic fluids, filters, and labor costs. The cost of both materials and labor varies with locality. Equipment manufacturers provide standard tables for estimating consumption of the above materials.

Repair Costs and the Repair Reserve. Repair costs include those for all parts and labor associated with each machine. Certain special-wear items are discussed under a separate heading.

Repairs are one of the highest, if not the highest, cost items under the heading of operating costs. Since they increase as a machine grows older, it is prudent to set aside funds for eventual repairs. Such funds are called the *repair reserve*. Again, manufacturers usually provide tables and charts that give average repair costs over the life of each machine. These tables and charts are usually accurate enough for operating cost estimates.

Tires. Tire costs can be expressed in the formula

$$\text{Hourly tire cost} = \frac{\text{tire replacement cost}}{\text{tire life (in hours)}}$$

Though usable, the formula is an oversimplification: actual tire cost varies widely and is difficult to estimate, except in a general manner. For example, different brands differ in cost and have varying life spans for the same use. Also, variable work surfaces and conditions make life spans hard to predict. Manufacturer's tables are perhaps the best source for estimating tire life under variable conditions.

Special-wear items. Some items on construction equipment receive extra-hard wear and thus wear out faster. Examples are the cutting edge or teeth of buckets, ripper tips, and grader cutting edges. Cranes are another such special-wear item in that they require much welding over years of use.

To help cut down on the costs of special-wear items, manufacturers offer replaceable teeth, edges, etc., so that the larger component does not have to be replaced in its entirety. The life span of such items depends on factors similar to those previously discussed for machines in general, i.e., operator techniques and working temperaments, type of work done, type of material being worked, etc. Manufacturers and/or local parts departments are a source of estimating information.

Operator's hourly wages. Local operator wage scales should be used in wage computations, including allowances for workmen's compensation and social security. Other compensation, e.g., fringe benefits, bonuses, and overtime, may also be appropriate in calculations.

Total owning and operating cost. As the name implies, this is the sum of all the owning and operating costs. It does *not*, however, include any figures for overhead; rather, it is a direct cost associated with machine ownership and operation. Many manufacturers, construction associations, contractors, and others have special formats or summary sheets for entering this cost. Figure 12–3 shows one such form.

Cost Per Cubic Yard

Production estimation calculations and past job experience data result in a simple figure, the *cost per cubic yard* it takes to move a material. This number is similar to a building contractor saying that it costs "$35 per square foot" (or whatever the cost per square foot might be) to build a certain tract house in a certain location. Cost per cubic yard is a simple, convenient number, but it is arrived at only after careful and detailed calculations relating to specific field conditions. Another way of expressing cost per cubic yard is the formula

$$\text{Cost/cubic yard} = \frac{\text{hourly owning and operating costs}}{\text{production per working hour}}$$

Machine Designation _____

OWNING COSTS

Depreciation $ _____ per hour

Interest
insurance, storage $ _____ per hour

Taxes, licenses,
freight, miscellaneous $ _____ per hour

                                                  Total $ _____/hr.

OPERATING COSTS

Fuel $ _____ per hour

Service costs $ _____ per hour

Repairs and repair reserve $ _____ per hour

Tires $ _____ per hour

Special wear items $ _____ per hour

                                                  Total $ _____/hr.

OPERATOR WAGES .... $ _____/hr.

TOTAL O & O COST .... $ _____/hr.

Figure 12–3. Individual contractors and manufacturers have their own forms for documenting and estimating owning and operating costs. This is a typical simple form.

Thus, if a machine's owning and operating costs are $60.00 per hour and the machine can deliver 100 cubic yards/hour on a certain job (after the efficiency factor has been included), then the cost per cubic yard equals $60.00/100 = .60 cents. That is, it will cost you 60 cents per cubic yard to move the material.

Cost Per Compacted Cubic Yard

When fill material is placed for construction purposes, it usually is installed in successive compacted layers until the desired elevation is reached. The thickness of the layers depends on the type of material and equipment used to compact it. Typical equipment includes pneumatic or rubber-tired rollers, drum-type rollers (such as the sheepsfoot roller), vibratory compactors, and smooth-drum rollers. All this equipment is available in a variety of sizes and weights.

Generally speaking, the heavier the compacting equipment used, the thicker the layers will be (other factors being equal). And, of course, the thicker the layers, the faster the job will be completed. In all cases, the layers must meet the compaction requirements of the job specifications, as determined by approved tests.

Production speed for compactors depends on four factors:

1. The width of the compactor
2. The travel speed of the machine
3. The thickness or *lift* of the compacted layer
4. The number of passes made

These factors enter into the following formula for determining production in compacted cubic yards per hour:

$$\text{Compacted cubic yards/hour} = \frac{W \times S \times L \times 16}{P}$$

where

$W =$ the width of the roller, in feet

$S =$ the travel speed of the machine, in miles/hour

$L =$ the lift of the compacted layer, in inches

$16 =$ a conversion constant

$P =$ the number of passes made

Example

A contractor must compact an area that will be used as a shopping center parking lot. The roller to be used has a width of 7 feet and can travel 10 miles/hour. The maximum thickness of each compacted layer is 4 inches, and the layers must be inspected by the consulting test laboratory before each successive layer may be installed. If it has been determined that the machine will have to make six passes to achieve the specified compaction and the job efficiency factor is estimated to be .80, how many compacted cubic yards may be installed per hour? If the owning and operating costs are estimated to be $30.00, what will it cost the contractor per cubic yard to compact the material?

Solution:

$$\text{Compacted cubic yards/hour} = \frac{W \times S \times L \times 16}{P}$$

$$= \frac{7 \text{ feet} \times 10 \text{ miles/hour} \times 4 \text{ inches} \times 16}{6} = 1,120$$

$$1{,}120 \text{ cubic yards/hour} \times .80 \text{ (efficiency factor)} = 896 \text{ cubic yards/hour}$$

$$\frac{\$30.00 \text{ (owning and operating cost/hour)}}{896 \text{ compacted cubic yards/hour}} = \frac{3.3 \text{ cents/compacted}}{\text{cubic yard}}$$

Another formula for the amount of material per hour that one piece of equipment can compact is

$$C = \frac{60 \text{ (minutes/hour)} \times S \times W \times D \times E}{N \times 27 \text{ (cubic feet/yard)}}$$

where

C = the number of compacted cubic yards of material per hour

S = the speed of the compactor, in feet per minute

W = the effective width of the roller/compactor, in feet

D = the depth of lift of the compactible material, in feet

E = the efficiency factor of the compactor

N = the number of passes made

This same formula may be used for variables expressed in metric units. That is, feet are replaced by meters, cubic yards per hour by cubic meters per hour and feet per minute by meters per minute.

In the following discussion of production estimation for specific pieces of equipment, it is suggested that the reader review the earlier discussions for that piece of equipment, focusing on the production techniques in particular.

Loader Production

Loader production is measured in either volume per hour or weight per hour. Typically, use volume (cubic yards) for earthmoving operations and weight (in tons) for quarry, pit, and similar operations. The reason for this is because volume is more likely to be the limiting factor in earth-moving operations and weight the limiting factor in quarry and pit operations.

If volume is used, then the amount the loader can carry per trip is simply the rated bucket capacity in yards. Production per hour may then be found by multiplying volume by trips per hour.

Example

A loader is estimated to have a cycle time of 2 minutes. The rated capacity of the bucket is 1.2 yards. What is the production per hour assuming an efficiency factor of .83 (a 50-minute hour)?

Solution:

$$\text{Trips/hour} = \frac{60 \text{ minutes}}{\text{cycle time in minutes}} = 60/2 = 30$$

$$
\begin{aligned}
\text{Production/hour} &= \text{trips/hours} \times \text{volume/trip} \times \text{efficiency} \\
&= 30 \times 1.2 \times .83 \\
&= 30 \text{ yards}
\end{aligned}
$$

If production is measured by weight, then production per hour may be found by multiplying weight in tons per trip by trips per hour by the efficiency factor.

The *bucket struck capacity* is the weight a machine is designed to carry with its bucket level, but not heaped full of material.

Example

A loader is estimated to have a cycle time of 2 minutes and a bucket struck capacity of 2 yards. If the material being carried is gravel from stockpile storage (3,200 lb/yard) and the efficiency factor is estimated to be .83, what will be the production per hour?

Solution:

$$\text{Bucket load} = \frac{\text{Weight of material/cubic yard} \times \text{bucket struck capacity}}{2,000 \text{ lb (ton)}}$$

$$= \frac{3,200 \text{ lb/yard} \times 2 \text{ yards}}{2,000 \text{ lb}} = 3.2 \text{ tons/trip}$$

$$\text{Trips/hour} = \frac{60 \text{ minutes}}{\text{cycle time in minutes}} = 60/2 = 30$$

$$\text{Production per hour} = 30 \text{ trips} \times 3.2 \text{ tons/trip} \times .83 \text{ (efficiency factor)} = 80 \text{ tons}$$

Motor Grader Production

Unlike haul units, the purpose of graders is not to transport materials from one location to another. However, graders are closely associated with haul equipment because they are usually the most efficient machine to maintain haul roads and other surfaces over which haul units move. The better the haul surfaces, the more efficient the haul units. Thus, it is appropriate to include graders in the category of production machinery.

The formula for grader production is

$$\text{Time (in hours)} = \frac{\text{Passes required} \times \text{distance (in miles)}}{\text{Speed in miles per hour} \times \text{hourly efficiency in each gear used}}$$

Example

A badly rutted haul road is ½ mile long by 36 feet wide. To maintain best production of the haul units, the haul road must be graded smooth. The available grader is equipped with a 12-foot blade. It is determined that three passes will be necessary in each of the first three gears (first one side of the road, then the middle portion, then the other side—the first gear handles the rough work, and then better speeds are attained for the finishing passes). How much time is spent in each gear, and what is the total amount of time required to complete the job?

Solution:

$$\text{Time in first gear} = \frac{3 \text{ passes} \times .5 \text{ mile}}{2.5 \text{ miles/hour} \times .83} = .72 \text{ hour}$$

$$\text{Time in second gear} = \frac{3 \text{ passes} \times .5 \text{ mile}}{4 \text{ miles/hour} \times .83} = .45 \text{ hour}$$

$$\text{Time in third gear} = \frac{3 \text{ passes} \times .5 \text{ mile}}{6 \text{ miles/hour} \times .83} = .30 \text{ hour}$$

Total time required to complete job $= .72 + .45 + .30 = 1.47$ hours

Dozer Production

Bulldozer production is estimated using production curves together with the correction factors that are applicable. The formula is

$$\begin{array}{l} \text{Production (loose cubic yards/hour)} \\ \text{(loose cubic meters/hour)} \end{array} = \begin{array}{c} \text{maximum} \\ \text{production} \end{array} \times \begin{array}{c} \text{correction} \\ \text{factors} \end{array}$$

The bulldozer production curves (see Figure 12–4) give maximum uncorrected production for straight and universal blades and are based on the following conditions:

1. 100% efficiency (60-minute hour).
2. Power shift machines with 0.05-minute fixed times.
3. Machine cuts for 50 feet (15 meters), then drifts blade load to dump over a high wall.
4. Soil density of 2,300 lb/loose cubic yard (1,370 kg/loose cubic meter).

ESTIMATED DOZING PRODUCTION • Universal and Straight Blades • D7 through D10

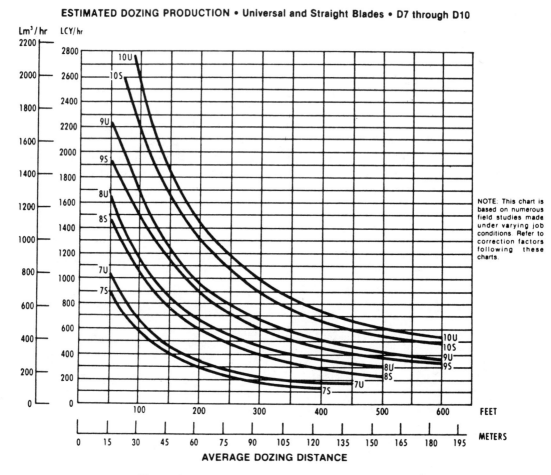

Figure 12–4. Dozer production curve. Source: Caterpillar.

5. Coefficient of traction:

   a. Track machines—0.5 or better

   b. Wheel machines—0.4 or better*

6. Use of hydraulically controlled blades.

*Coefficient of traction is assumed to be at least 0.4. While poor traction affects both track and wheeled vehicles, causing them to take smaller blade loads, wheeled units are affected more severely and production falls much more rapidly. While no fixed rules can predict this production loss, a rough rule of thumb is that wheeled dozer production falls off 4% for each one-hundredth decrease in coefficient of traction below 0.40. If, for example, the coefficient of traction is 0.30, the difference is ten-hundredths (0.10), and production is 60% ($10 \times 4\% = 40\%$ decrease).

To obtain estimated production in bank cubic yards or bank cubic meters, the appropriate load factor should be applied to the corrected production as calculated above.

$$\text{Production (bank cubic yards/hour)} \atop \text{(bank cubic meters/hour)} = \frac{\text{(loose cubic yards/hour)} \times \text{LF}}{\text{(loose cubic meters/hour)} \times \text{LF}}$$

Ripper Production

The best way to estimate ripper production is to conduct field tests on enough segments of the site to determine what average production will be for the whole. If field tests utilizing rippers are not practicable, other field tests offer some insight into ripper productivity. Samples removed with a coal drill, for instance, or test pits (usually dug with a relatively small backhoe) are indicative. Seismic investigations are also often useful.

Seismic analysis of ripper productivity is conducted by measuring the time required for a receiver to pick up sound waves produced by a minor explosion or hammer blow on the site at a known distance from the receiver. Sound travel times have been conducted for many materials, so that fairly accurate estimates of ripper productivity may be derived from seismographic results. (See Figure 12–5.)

Again, once it is determined that a ripper can be productively employed at the site, the best way to estimate production is through actual field testing of the equipment. The following formula may be used to measure ripping production:

$$P = \frac{2 \times D \times W \times L \times E}{T}$$

where

P = production

D = average penetration, in feet

W = average width loosened, in feet*

L = length of pass, in feet

E = job efficiency factor

T = cycle time, including stalls, slippage, turns, etc.

*This quantity will vary with number of shanks, different strengths of the shanks, different manufacturers, etc.

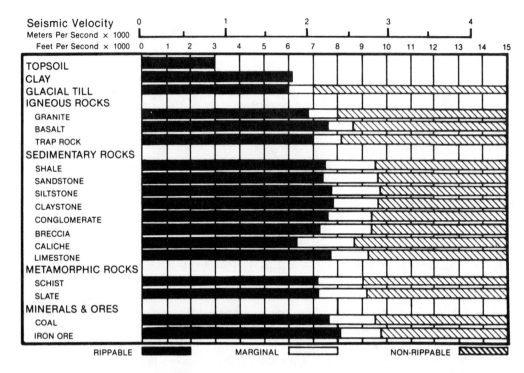

Figure 12–5. Caterpillar D8L ripper performance estimated by seismic-wave velocities.

If no field tests of any kind can be performed, the constructor may make use of production graphs that are keyed to specific machines and rippers. These graphs are helpful for quick estimates. (See Figure 12–6.*)

Backhoe Production

To estimate backhoe production, we must be able to predict cycle time and average bucket payload. Many factors influence cycle time, including:

*The following considerations are applicable to the production graph in the figure:
- The machine rips full time; that is, no dozing is performed.
- Power shift tractors with single-shank rippers are used.
- 100% efficiency (a 60-minute hour) is shown.
- The graphs are for all classes of material.
- In igneous rock with seismic velocity of 6,000 feet per second or higher, the production figures shown should be reduced by 25%.
- The upper limit of the graph reflects ripping under ideal conditions only. If other factors exist (such as thick lamination, vertical lamination, etc.) which would adversely affect production, the lower limit should be used.

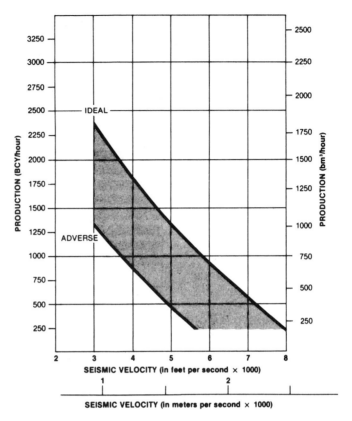

Figure 12–6. Ripping production estimating graph for Caterpillar D8L with single shank. Source: Caterpillar

1. Size of the machine and bucket
2. Depth of excavation
3. Material to be excavated
4. Dump point (truck, spoil pile, or other)
5. Obstacles on the site (utilities, shoring, people, etc.)
6. Operator skill

Some manufacturers produce cycle time charts for various conditions. These charts are general in nature, so that the manager must take into account the actual job conditions when using such data. If cycle time charts are not available, field tests for cycle time are relatively quick and inexpensive for backhoes. (See Figure 12–7.)

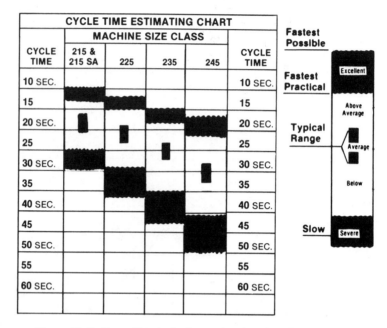

Figure 12–7. Caterpillar cycle time estimating chart for backhoes.

Average bucket payload is fairly easy to come by: manufacturers give bucket specifications, and, once the characteristics of the material are known, bucket capacities may be determined. The following formula may be used to calculate average bucket payload:

Average bucket payload = heaped bucket capacity × bucket fill factor

The table below shows bucket fill factors for some common materials:

MATERIAL	PERCENT OF HEAPED BUCKET CAPACITY
Moist loam or sandy clay	100–110%
Sand and gravel	95–100%
Hard, tough clay	80–90%
Rock, well blasted	60–75%
Rock, poorly blasted	40–50%

Once theoretical or field-measured estimates of cycle time and average bucket payload are made, the following formula may be used to estimate backhoe production:

Cubic yards/60-minute hour = cycles/60-minute hour × average bucket payload

This formula represents 100% efficiency (a 60-minute hour); therefore, the answer must be multiplied by the appropriate job efficiency factor to estimate actual production.

Scraper Production

Scrapers are composite machines, performing some of the functions of loaders and some of the functions of hauling equipment. They neither load as well as machines built specifically for loading nor haul as well as machines built specifically for hauling. Their advantage, however, lies in their ability to perform both loading and hauling functions under certain site and soil conditions.

Site and soil conditions also influence the selection of the particular type of scraper(s) to be used. Typical scraper configurations include:

1. Crawler-tractor pulled
2. Rubber-tired tractor pulled
3. Single engine
4. Twin engine
5. Single bowl
6. Multibowl (two or more bowls arranged in line, typically with multi-engine and/or tractor push assistance)
7. Elevating scraper
8. Other configurations or combinations of configurations

As usual, crawler units are used where traction or other site conditions make the use of the faster rubber-tired units impractical.

The removal or loosening of rocks, roots, and other obstacles by the appropriate machines usually contributes to the overall loading and hauling efficiency of scrapers. Performance charts for wheeled scrapers are available from the manufacturers. Together with the machine specifications, these charts provide a quick way of evaluating a scraper's performance under various job conditions.

Figure 12–8 shows a scraper, the specifications of which are as follows:

862 SCRAPER SPECIFICATIONS

(Specifications and design subject to change without notice. Wherever applicable, specifications are in accordance with ICED and SAE Standards. Except where otherwise noted, these specifications are based on a unit equipped with 26.5-25, 24-PR tires, ROPS canopy, full fuel tank, 175 lb. (79 kg) operator, and all standard equipment.)

Capacity (SAE heaped):

Volume ....16 cu. yd. (12.23 m³)
Total weight of payload ....40,000 lb. (18 144 kg)
  2500 lb./yd.³ (1483 kg/m³)

Power (@ 2100 engine rpm):	SAE	DIN
Gross	270 hp (201 kW)	250 hp (186 kW)
Net		186 kW

Net engine power is with standard equipment including air cleaner, exhaust system, alternator and cooling fan. Gross power is without cooling. Power ratings are at standard conditions per SAE J1349 and DIN 70 020. No derating is required up to 7500 feet (2290 m) altitude.

Engine: John Deere turbocharged and intercooled diesel, 6-cylinder, 4-stroke cycle

Bore and stroke ....5.12x5 in. (130x127 mm)
Piston displacement ....619 cu. in. (10.145 L)
Compression ratio ....15.2 to 1
Maximum torque @ 1400 rpm ...813 lb-ft (1102 kg-m)
NACC or AMA (U.S. Tax) horsepower 62.9
Main bearings 7
Lubrication ....Pressure system w/full-flow filter
Cooling ....Pressurized w/thermostat and controlled bypass
Fan ....Suction
Aspirated air cleaner w/safety element and restriction indicator ....Dry
Electrical system ....24-volt w/alternator
Batteries (two 12 volt) ....Reserve capacity: 180 minutes

Torque Converter:

Two-phase single stage with 2.84 to 1 multiplication ratio, free-wheeling stator lockup clutch and automatic control.

Transmission:

Planetary Power Shift, 6 forward, 1 reverse speeds. Microprocessor controlled, fully automatic shift with modulation.

Gear pump ....32 gpm (2.0 L/s) @ 2100 rpm for transmission lubrication, torque converter charge and transmission shift actuation.

Filtration
All systems are protected by replaceable filters.

Main hydraulic system	10-micron filters
Elevator system	10-micron filters
Transmission	10-micron filters
Engine	25-micron filters
Differential	10-micron filters

Hydraulic Cylinders:

	Bore	Stroke
Lift (2)	5 in. (127 mm)	20 in. (508 mm)
Sliding floor (1)	5.25 in. (133 mm)	38.8 in. (986 mm)
Ejector gate (2)	3 in. (76 mm)	49.0 in. (1244 mm)
Steering (2)	4 in. (102 mm)	25.9 in. (658 mm)

Piston rods ....Ground, heat-treated, chrome-plated, polished
Lift and steering cylinders ....2 in. (51 mm) dia.
Sliding floor cylinder ....2.5 in. (64 mm) dia.
Ejector gate cylinders ....1.75 in. (44 mm) dia.

Elevator ....Reversible, hydrostatic drive with heavy-duty planetary reduction. A sealed chain is standard for extended life. A non-sealed chain is optional.

Number of flights 23
Spacing of flights ....12.52 in. (318 mm)
Width of flights ....6 ft. 6 in. (1.98 m)
Speed (@ 2100 engine rpm) .....0-240 fpm (73 m/min)
Length (top to bottom) ....12 ft. (3.66 mm)

Bowl ....Heavy-gauge steel with reinforcing and box construction. Sliding floor rides on heat-treated rails. Cutting edge retracts. Independent rear axles are vertically adjustable.

Cutting Edge ....8 ft. 9.9 in. (2.69 m) wide; 3 sections, reversible and replaceable, high-carbon steel. Each section is adjustable vertically 2 in. (51 mm).

Center section ....1x13x77.9 in. (25x330x1979 mm)
End sections ....1x13x14 in. (25x330x356 mm)

Tires:

26.5-25, steel-cord radials
26.5-25, 24-PR, E2
26.5-29, steel-cord radials
26.5-29, 26-PR, E2

Figure 12–8. Performance chart for John Deere 862 scraper.

Differential Lock .... Foot-operated, hydraulically actuated

Drive Axle ..... Differential drive; over-all ratio 22.22 to 1; planetary final drives with 4.4 gpm (0.28 L/s) pump for axle lubrication and differential lock actuation

Brakes: Hydraulic; power actuated. An accumulator provides several brake applications after engine is stopped.
Tractor .... Wet-disk between differential and planetaries. No adjustment needed.
Scraper .... Expanding shoe, self-adjusting, in wheels.
Parking ...... Manually controlled, mechanical, on axle input shaft.

Power Steering: Position-responsive

Articulated frame hydraulically actuated by dual cylinders.
Turning circle (180 deg. turn) .... 32 ft. 9.9 in. (10.0 m)
Articulation .... 180 deg.

Tractor Oscillation (total) .... 40 deg.

Hydraulic Systems:
Main tractor system: Closed-center
System pressure .... 2350 psi (16 203 kPa) (165.2 kg/cm²)
Operates steering, brakes, and all scraper functions except elevator drive.
Main pump .... Variable displacement, constant pressure; delivers 63 gpm (3.97 L/s) @ 2100 engine rpm. Main charge pump delivers 20.3 gpm (1.28 L/s) @ 2100 engine rpm.
Elevator system .... Engine-driven, 5.43 cu. in. (89 cm³) variable displacement, reversible hydrostatic pump delivers 53.5 gpm (3.38 L/s) @ 2100 engine rpm.
System pressure .... 5000 psi (34 475 kPa) (351 kg/cm²)

Capacities

	U.S.	Liters
Cooling system	15 gal.	56.8
Fuel tank	110 gal.	416.4
Engine lubrication, including filter	31 qt.	29.3
Transmission case and filter	19 gal.	71.9
Differential case	7.5 gal.	28.4
Hydraulic reservoir	24 gal.	90.8
Elevator gear case	8 qt.	7.6

Additional Standard Equipment:

Cigaret lighter
Deluxe suspension seat
Ether starting aid
Fenders (tractor and scraper)
Gauges:
 Voltmeter
 Engine oil pressure
 Engine water temperature
 Fuel
 Hourmeter
 Hydrostatic charge pressure
 Speedometer
 Tachometer
 Transmission lube pressure
 Transmission oil pressure
 Transmission oil temperature
 Elevator charge pressure
Hitch, steering and rear frame central lube systems
Horn
Horizontal muffler
Indicator warning lights:
 Brake pressure
 Hydraulic filter
 Parking brake light and buzzer
 Transmission filter
Lights (head and work)
Reverse warning alarm
ROPS canopy and seat belt
Windshield w/wiper
Turn signals and 4-way flasher
Vandal protection

Weight Distribution:

		lb.	kg
Empty:	Drive axle	32,050	14 538
	Scraper axle	17,139	7774
	Total	49,189	22 312
Loaded:	Drive axle	44,400	20 140
	Scraper axle	44,789	20 316
	Total	89,189	40 456

Special Equipment:
Air conditioner
Cab panels
Fender extensions and mud flaps for scraper wheels
Heater
Teeth for cutting edge

(Continued on next page).

Figure 12–8. (Continued).

862 SCRAPER VEHICLE PERFORMANCE

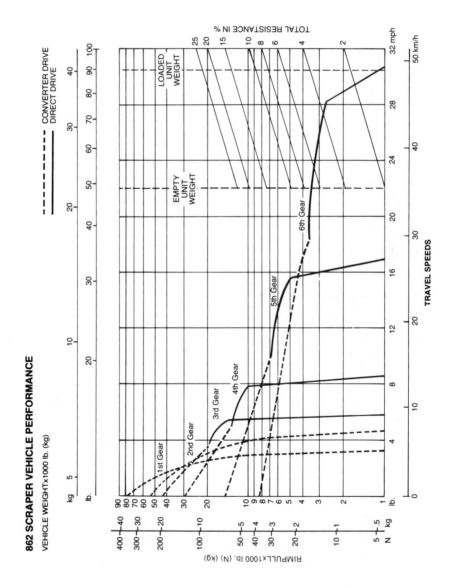

Figure 12–8. (Continued).

To use the figure to calculate performance, read down from vehicle weight to the percent of total resistance. (Total resistance is the actual percent of grade plus one percent for each 20 pounds per ton of rolling resistance.) Then, from this weight-resistance point, read straight across to the curve with the highest obtainable speed range, and then down to the maximum speed.

Remember that usable rimpull is affected by both traction available and weight on the drive wheels.

As is typical with most earthmoving jobs, production may be estimated by multiplying the average load per cycle by the number of cycles estimated per unit of time (usually per hour). To estimate the number of cycles per hour and get the total cycle time, we must break the cycle time into fixed cycle time and variable cycle time. The equation is

$$\text{Total cycle time} = \text{fixed cycle time} + \text{variable cycle time}$$

Fixed time is that time devoted to tasks other than hauling and returning. It is most accurately arrived at by field tests, but tables, such as Table 12–8 (produced by Caterpillar for its scrapers), are helpful for off-the-job estimates. Variable time, the actual time required to haul and return, depends on the distance traveled and the speed of the machine under job conditions. Hauling and returning are typically done at different speeds due to weight changes and perhaps route changes. Obviously, the machine will ordinarily travel faster empty than fully loaded. Route changes may mean differences in the difficulty of travel and thus different speeds. Therefore, it is usually necessary to compute

Table 12–8. Typical fixed times for scrapers. (Times may vary depending on job conditions.) This table, for Caterpillar scrapers, provides quick estimates of fixed times. More accurate estimates may be obtained by actual field tests.

MODEL	LOADED BY	LOAD TIME (MIN.)	MANEUVER AND SPREAD OR MANEUVER AND DUMP (MIN.)
613B	Self-loading	0.9	0.7
615	Self-loading	0.9	0.7
621B	One D8L	0.7	0.7
623B	Self-loading	0.9	0.7
627B	One D8L	0.6	0.6
627B/PP	Self-loading	0.8*	0.7
631D	One D9L	0.6	0.7
633D	Self-loading	0.9	0.7
637D	One D9L	0.5	0.6
637D/PP	Self-loading	0.9*	0.7
639D	Self-loading	0.9	0.7
651B	Two D9L's	0.6	0.7
657B	Two D9L's	0.4	0.6
657B/PP	Self-loading	1.0	0.7

*Load time per pair, including transfer time
Source: Caterpillar Tractor Company

haul time and return time separately, and then average the speed for the whole route or cycle.

As an example, suppose we wish to compute the cycle time required for a scraper to haul earth from a pit to a fill area 3,000 feet away and back. Suppose further that fixed-time conditions are average—that is, there are no extraordinary physical obstacles to restrict movement of the machine. Then, noting the grade, traction, and other site conditions, we determine from the manufacturer's performance charts and specifications that the scraper can haul the material at an average speed of 13 miles per hour and return empty to the pit at an average speed of 26 miles per hour. Further, checking the fixed-time chart, we find that the total time required to load, maneuver, spread, and dump is 1.7 minutes. Thus,

$$\text{Fixed time} = 1.7 \text{ minutes}$$

$$\text{Haul time} = \frac{3,000}{13 \times 88} = 2.6 \text{ minutes}$$

$$\text{Return time} = \frac{3,000}{26 \times 88} = 1.3 \text{ minutes}$$

$$\text{Total cycle time} = (1.7 + 2.6 + 1.3) \text{ minutes} = 5.6 \text{ minutes}$$

Now, production per hour equals trips per hour times volume of material hauled. Trips per hour is $60/5.6 = 10.7$. However, this represents 100% efficiency (a 60-minute hour), which is impossible. If job and management conditions imply, say, a 50-minute hour, then trips per hour is $50/5.6 = 8.9$. If the scraper hauls 44 cubic yards per trip, production per hour is then 8.9×44 cubic yards, or approximately 392 cubic yards per hour.

Shovel and Dragline Production

Hydraulic shovel. The loading cycle of the hydraulic shovel is similar to that of the backhoe, and the bucket fill factors are the same as well. Thus, production may be estimated just as for backhoes, that is, by using manufacturers' estimates of cycle time or by field testing, and by figuring average bucket payload, etc.

Cable-operated diesel-powered shovel. The Power Crane and Shovel Association of the Construction Industry Manufacturers Association (CIMA) has assembled data on shovel production through the years and has compiled a set of interdependent tables to simplify production estimation. *Ideal output values* are based on a 90-degree swing, an optimum depth of cut of material, the material being loaded into haul units at grade level, and 100% efficiency. *Optimum depth cuts* for the machine and material are divided into *actual depth* of cut on the job to obtain a percent, which is then applied to the *swing–depth factor* table. The formula for production then becomes

$$\text{Production} = \text{ideal output} \times \text{swing–depth factor} \times \text{efficiency}$$

As always, efficiency depends on both physical job conditions and management job conditions. Typical physical job conditions include weather, surface conditions, and work space. Typical management job conditions include operator skill and attitudes, management skill and attitudes, and maintenance of equipment.

The following efficiency factors are accurate enough for general estimating purposes. However, actual job conditions must always be kept in mind when using such figures.

	MANAGEMENT CONDITIONS			
PHYSICAL CONDITIONS	VERY GOOD	GOOD	FAIR	POOR
very good	0.84	0.81	0.76	0.70
good	0.78	0.75	0.71	0.65
fair	0.72	0.69	0.65	0.60
poor	0.63	0.61	0.57	0.52

Remember that efficiency factors such as those shown are percentages of an hour. Thus, a contractor who estimates the work hour at 50 minutes is estimating an efficiency factor of .83 (that is, 50 minutes/60 minutes).

Example

A shovel with a capacity of 3 cubic yards is to be used to excavate sandy loam. The job requires a 60-degree swing angle and an average depth of cut of 12 feet. Physical site conditions are fair, and the operator and management are very good. How many bank cubic yards per hour can the contractor expect to excavate?

Solution:

Ideal output (from Table 12–9) = 465 bank cubic yards/hour

Optimum depth of cut (from Table 12–10) = 8.8 feet

$$\frac{\text{Actual depth of cut}}{\text{Optimum depth of cut}} = \frac{12 \text{ feet}}{8.8 \text{ feet}} = 1.4 = 140\%$$

Swing–depth factor (from Table 12–11) = 1.04

Efficiency factor (from table above) = 0.72

Table 12–9. Ideal shovel output in BCY/hr. These figures are derived from the experience of the PCSA, a bureau of the Construction Industry Manufacturers Association. The figures are based on 100% efficiency, 90-degree swing, optimum depth of cut, material loaded into haul units at grade level.

TYPE OF MATERIAL	SHOVEL DIPPER SIZE IN CUBIC YARDS											
	¾	1	1¼	1½	1¾	2	2½	3	3½	4	4½	5
Moist loam or light sandy clay	165	205	250	285	320	355	405	465	525	580	635	685
Sand and gravel	155	200	230	270	300	330	390	450	505	555	600	645
Common earth	135	175	210	240	270	300	355	405	455	510	560	605
Tough clay, hard	110	145	180	210	235	265	310	360	405	450	490	530
Well-blasted rock	95	125	155	180	205	230	275	320	365	410	455	500
Wet, sticky clay	70	95	120	145	165	185	230	270	310	345	385	420
Poorly blasted rock	50	75	95	115	140	160	195	235	270	305	340	375

Table 12–10. Optimum depth of cut for shovels in feet. Based on PCSA figures.

TYPE OF MATERIAL	DIPPER SIZE IN CUBIC YARDS											
	¾	1	1¼	1½	1¾	2	2½	3	3½	4	4½	5
Loam, sand, gravel, and similar free-flowing materials	5.3	6.0	6.5	7.0	7.4	7.8	8.4	8.8	9.1	9.4	9.7	10.0
Common earth and similar medium-type materials	6.8	7.8	8.5	9.2	9.7	10.2	11.2	12.1	13.0	13.8	14.7	15.5
Tough and/or sticky clays and soils and similar harder materials; also rocky soils and blasted rock	8.0	9.0	9.8	10.7	11.5	12.2	13.3	14.2	15.1	16.0	16.9	17.8

Table 12–11. Swing–depth factor for shovels. Based on PCSA figures.

DEPTH OF CUT (% OF OPTIMUM)	ANGLE OF SWING						
	45°	60°	75°	90°	120°	150°	180°
40	0.93	0.89	0.85	0.80	0.72	0.65	0.59
60	1.10	1.03	0.96	0.91	0.81	0.73	0.66
80	1.22	1.12	1.04	0.98	0.86	0.77	0.69
100	1.26	1.16	1.07	1.00	0.88	0.79	0.71
120	1.20	1.11	1.03	0.97	0.86	0.77	0.70
140	1.12	1.04	0.97	0.91	0.81	0.73	0.66
160	1.03	0.96	0.90	0.85	0.75	0.67	0.62

$$\text{Estimated production} = \text{ideal output} \times \text{swing–depth factor}$$
$$\times \text{efficiency factor}$$

$$= 465 \text{ bank cubic yards/hour} \times 1.04 \times 0.72$$
$$= 348 \text{ bank cubic yards/hour}$$

Dragline production is computed exactly like shovel production, but using the dragline tables (PCSA; Tables 12–12, 12–13, and 12–14) instead of shovel tables. The efficiency table is the same as that for shovel production.

Example

A dragline with a capacity of ¾ cubic yard is to be used to excavate common earth. The job requires a 60-degree swing angle and an average depth of cut of 8 feet. Physical site conditions are good, as are the operator and management. How many loose cubic yards per hour can the contractor expect to excavate?

Solution:

Ideal output (from Table 12–12) = 105 bank cubic yards/hour

Optimum depth of cut (from Table 12–13) = 7.4 feet

$$\frac{\text{Actual depth of cut}}{\text{Optimum depth of cut}} = \frac{8 \text{ feet}}{7.4 \text{ feet}} = 1.1 = 110\%$$

Swing–depth factor (from Table 12–14) = 1.10 (interpolate from the table)

Efficiency factor (from table on p. 207) = 0.75

$$\text{Estimated production} = \text{ideal output} \times \text{swing–depth factor}$$
$$\times \text{efficiency}$$

$$= 105 \text{ bank cubic yards/hour} \times 1.10 \times 0.75$$
$$= 86.6 \text{ bank cubic yards/hour}$$

The conversion factor for bank to loose yards for common earth is 1.25. Thus, 86.6 bank cubic yards/hour × 1.25 = 108 loose cubic yards/hour

Clamshell production

Hydraulic clamshell. Production estimation for the hydraulic clamshell is similar to that for the backhoe. The clamshell usually just replaces the backhoe attachment. Otherwise, the cycle movements are the same: load, swing, dump, and return.

Cable-operated clamshells. Cable-operated clamshells are the machines with which we are primarily concerned here. These machines present more difficulty in production estimation than do hydraulic machines performing similar

Table 12–12. Ideal output for short boom dragline in BCY/hr. Based on PCSA figures.

TYPE OF MATERIAL	BUCKET SIZE IN CUBIC YARDS										
	¾	1	1¼	1½	1¾	2	2½	3	3½	4	5
Loam or light moist clay	130	160	195	220	245	265	305	350	390	465	540
Sand, gravel	125	155	185	210	235	255	295	340	380	455	530
Common earth	105	135	165	190	210	230	265	305	340	375	445
Clay, tough	90	110	135	160	180	195	230	270	305	340	410
Clay, wet and sticky	55	75	95	110	130	145	175	210	240	270	330

Table 12–13. Optimum depth of cut for draglines in feet. Based on PCSA figures.

TYPE OF MATERIAL	BUCKET SIZE IN CUBIC YARDS										
	¾	1	1¼	1½	1¾	2	2½	3	3½	4	5
Loam, light moist clay, sand, gravel	6.0	6.6	7.0	7.4	7.7	8.0	8.5	9.0	9.5	10.0	11.0
Common earth	7.4	8.0	8.5	9.0	9.5	9.9	10.5	11.0	11.5	12.0	13.0
Clay, tough or wet and sticky	8.7	9.3	10.0	10.7	11.3	11.8	12.3	12.8	13.3	13.8	14.3

Table 12–14. Swing–depth factor for draglines. Based on PCSA figures.

DEPTH OF CUT (% OF OPTIMUM)	ANGLE OF SWING							
	30°	45°	60°	75°	90°	120°	150°	180°
20	1.06	0.99	0.94	0.90	0.87	0.81	0.75	0.70
40	1.17	1.08	1.02	0.97	0.93	0.85	0.78	0.72
60	1.25	1.13	1.06	1.01	0.97	0.88	0.80	0.74
80	1.29	1.17	1.09	1.04	0.99	0.90	0.82	0.76
100	1.32	1.19	1.11	1.05	1.00	0.91	0.83	0.77
120	1.29	1.17	1.09	1.03	0.98	0.90	0.82	0.76
140	1.25	1.14	1.06	1.00	0.96	0.88	0.81	0.75
160	1.20	1.10	1.02	0.97	0.93	0.85	0.79	0.73
180	1.15	1.05	0.98	0.94	0.90	0.82	0.76	0.71
200	1.10	1.00	0.94	0.90	0.87	0.79	0.73	0.69

work, primarily because it is difficult to estimate cycle time because of the way the bucket is loaded. That is, the bucket may tip over when it hits an obstacle or may otherwise have to be lifted and dropped again. Other variables in production estimation of the machine include:

1. Size of load obtainable
2. Dump point (truck, hopper, spoil pile, or other)
3. Height of lift and angle of swing
4. Operator skill (good operators should swing and lift the load at the same time; if they don't, the cycle time is increased)

Generally speaking, if field tests are not possible, the crane specifications must be studied carefully and reviewed against job needs. Relevant questions are:

1. What is the weight of the bucket? (The weight affects the total load the crane can lift.)
2. What is the angle of swing?
3. What is the speed of the hoist line?
4. What is the swing speed?

Essentially, the clamshell cycle consists of:

1. Loading the bucket
2. Lifting the load
3. Swinging the load
4. Lowering the bucket
5. Estimating lost time

To compute cycle time, we must know the machine specifications and the job conditions and requirements. As with crane specifications, there are several relevant questions:

1. What is the bucket capacity?
2. What distance must the load be lifted or lowered? (The distance multiplied by the speed of the hoist line will give us this phase of the cycle.)
3. What swing angle is necessary to do the job?
4. What is the swing speed of the machine?

5. What is the estimated time lost due to observed or known job conditions such as heavy rocks in the soil, and the like? Common sense and attention to details are the main factors in figuring cycle time for the clamshell.

When cycle time is estimated, the following equation applies:

$$\text{Estimated production} = \text{cycles/hour} \times \text{average load} \times \text{efficiency factor}$$

Truck and Wagon Production

The production of trucks and wagons depends on the size of the load and the number of cycles per hour. The latter in turn depends on the vehicle weight, weight of the load, power, haul distance, and type of haul road. Usually, it is cost effective to balance the number and capacities of the haul units with the number and capacities of the excavating units. By so doing, the ideal of a continuous, uniform excavating and hauling cycle will be more nearly met. A common rule of thumb in the industry is that the truck capacity should be a minimum of four to five times the capacity of the excavator bucket or dipper when a dragline or shovel is used. Table 12–15 gives a rough idea of the number of haul units needed per hour for a given size of excavator.

Production rates for haul units may be computed similarly to those for rubber-tired tractors and scrapers,—that is, by computing rolling resistance, grade resistance, total resistance, rimpull required, etc., and applying these factors to job conditions. Most manufacturers give all the specifications needed, including:

Table 12–15. *Number of trucks or haul units needed to be spotted per hour under shovel in medium digging. Table is based on 100% efficiency factor for shovel or dipper, 90° swing, no delay, loading on grade.*

SIZE SHOVEL DIGGER (CU YD)	APPROX SHOVEL CYCLE TIME (IN SECONDS)	LOADING TIME FOR 4-DIPPER TRUCK (IN SECONDS)	INTERVAL (IN MINUTES) FOR SPOTTING TRUCKS	NUMBER OF TRUCKS NEEDED AT THE SHOVEL PER HOUR
⅜	18	72	1.2	50
½	18	72	1.2	50
¾	20	80	1.33	45
1	20	80	1.33	45
1¼	20	80	1.33	45
1½	20	80	1.33	45
2	20	80	1.33	45
2½	22	88	1.46	41

Source: U.S. Army

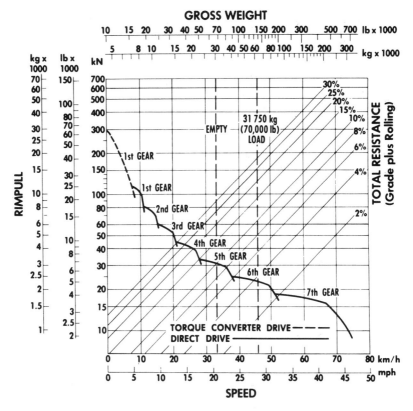

Figure 12–9. Rimpull–Speed–Gradeability chart for Caterpillar 769C truck. If gross vehicle weight and total resistance are known, machine speed attainable, gear range, and available rimpull can be found using this chart. Source: Caterpillar.

1. Payload capacity

2. Horsepower

3. Weight when empty

4. Total weight capacity

5. Volume capacity

6. Weight distribution

7. Fixed times

8. Other information needed to compute haul capacity

Manufacturers' performance charts are also available which make quick production estimates possible. (See Figure 12–9.) To use the chart, read gross weight down to percent of total resistance. From this intersection, read horizontally across to the curve with highest obtainable speed, and then down to the maximum speed. Keep in mind that usable rimpull depends on both traction and weight on the drive wheels. Similar charts are available for favorable grades.

Water Distributor and Compactor Production*

Step 1: In determining the number of water distributors required to support compaction operations when adding water on a fill site area, first determine the area covered by one distributor.

$$\text{Area covered (sq yd)} = \frac{\text{distributor capacity (gal)}}{\text{gal required/sq yd}}$$

Step 2: Determine the length of this area:

$$\text{Length of area covered (ft)} = \frac{\text{area covered (sq yd)} \times 3}{\text{spraybar length (yd)}}$$

Step 3: Determine the time required for spraying:

$$\text{Distributing time (min)} = \frac{\text{length of area covered (ft)}}{\text{speed of distributor (ft/min)}}$$

Step 4: Determine the total distribution cycle time:

$$\text{Cycle time} = \text{travel time} + \text{loading time} + \text{distributing time}$$

Step 5: Determine the hourly output of one distributor:

$$\text{Hourly output} = \frac{60 \text{ (min/hr)} \times \text{distributor capacity}}{\text{cycle time (min)}}$$

Step 6: Determine the number of distributors required:

$$\text{Number distributors required per hour} = \frac{\text{gallons required per hour}}{\text{hourly output of one distributor}}$$

The amount of material that one piece of compaction equipment can compact is then given by

*Source: U.S. Army TM5-331A, Aug., 1967

$$C = \frac{60 \ (\text{min/hr}) \times S \times W \times D \times E}{N \times 27 \ (\text{cu ft/yd})}$$

where

C = Compaction in (1) cu yd/hr or (2) cu meters/hr

S = Speed of compactor in (1) ft/min or (2) meters/min

W = Effective width of roller/compactor in (1) feet or (2) meters

D = Depth of lift in (1) feet or (2) meters

E = Efficiency factor of the compactor

N = Number of passes

Example

A project requires the placing of 1,000,000 cubic yards of earth for a dam. The job conditions are as follows:

Class of earth: sandy clay, 2,400 lb/cu yd *bank* measure, swell is 25 percent, compaction is 85 percent
Initial moisture content: 7 percent by weight
Required moisture content: 12 percent by weight
Maximum lift thickness: 6 inches compacted
Number of passes required (sheepsfoot roller): 12
Average distance to water: 1 mile
Earth hauling capability: 600 cu yd (compacted) per hour.

Find the number of (1) graders required for spreading, (2) water distributors required for wetting the material, and (3) rollers required for compacting the fill.

(1) *Spreading*.

$$\text{Area covered per hour} = 2 \times 600 \ \text{cu yd} \times 27 \ \text{cu ft/yd}$$

$$= 32,400 \ \text{sq ft}$$

Using a 100-hp grader with 12-foot blade; average speed including turns, stops, etc. = 2 mph; effective width of blade = 9 feet; estimated number of passes per layer = 4.

$$\text{Area covered per hour (one pass)} = \frac{2 \ \text{mph} \times 5,280 \ \text{ft/mi} \times 9 \ \text{ft/pass} \times 50 \ \text{min}}{60 \ \text{min/hr}}$$

$$= 79,300 \text{ sq ft}$$

$$\text{Area covered per hour, 4 passes} = \frac{79,300}{4} = 19,825 \text{ sq ft}$$

$$\text{Number of graders required} = \frac{32,400}{19,825} = 1.6 \text{ or 2 graders}$$

(2) *Wetting the material.*

$$\text{Weight of earth placed per hour} = \frac{600 \text{ cu yd} \times 2,400 \text{ lb/yd}}{.85 \text{ (\% compaction)}}$$

$$= 1,694,000 \text{ lb}$$

$$\text{Water to be added (by weight)} = 12 - 7 = 5 \text{ percent}$$

$$\text{Quantity of water required} = \frac{1,694,000 \text{ lb} \times 0.05 \text{ (percent)}}{8.33 \text{ lb/gal}}$$

$$= 10,170 \text{ gal}$$

Use water trucks with 1,000-gal capacity
Loading pump will deliver 250 gal/min
The round trip time per truck will be—

$$\text{Loading time} = \frac{1,000 \text{ gal}}{250 \text{ gpm}} = 4.00 \text{ min}$$

$$\text{Hauling time} = \frac{1 \text{ mi} \times 60 \text{ min/hr}}{15 \text{ mph}} = 4.00 \text{ min}$$

$$\text{Sprinkling time} = \frac{1,000 \text{ gal}}{150 \text{ gpm}} = 6.67 \text{ min}$$

$$\text{Return time} = \frac{1 \text{ mi} \times 60 \text{ min/hr}}{20 \text{ mph}} = 3.00 \text{ min}$$

Fixed time $= 3.33$ min

Total time $= 4.00 + 4.00 + 6.67 + 3.00 + 3.33 = 21.00$ min

$$\text{Trips per 50-min hr} = \frac{50}{21} = 2.38$$

$$\text{Quantity hauled per truck per hour} = 2.38 \times 1,000 = 2,380 \text{ gal}$$

$$\text{Number of trucks required} = \frac{\text{gallons required}}{\text{gallons/truck/hour}}$$

$$= \frac{10,170}{2,380} = 4.27 \text{ or } 5 \text{ trucks}$$

(3) *Compacting the fill.*

Weight of 3-drum roller $= 21,570$ lb

Width of roller $= 12$ feet

Power required $= 600$ DBPP* per ton of weight

$= 600$ DBPP $\times 11$ tons $= 6,000$ DBPP required

Use a crawler tractor, 5th gear, 9,490 DBPP at 5.2 mph

$$\text{Compaction} = \frac{60 \text{ min/hr} \times .83 \times (5.2 \text{ mph} \times 88)}{12 \times 27 \text{ cu ft/cu yd}} \times 12 \text{ ft} \times 0.5 \text{ ft}$$

$$= 422 \text{ cu yd/hr}$$

$$\text{Number of rollers required} = \frac{600}{422} = 1.4 \text{ or } 2 \text{ rollers}$$

(4) Balanced team consists of—

Spreading .... 2 graders

Wetting .... 5 water distributors, 1,000-gal

Compacting .... 2 sheepsfoot rollers, 3-drum, with tractors

FIGURING PRODUCTION ON THE JOB**

Load Weighing

The most accurate method of determining the actual load carried is by weighing. For haul units this is normally done by weighing one wheel or axle at a time using portable scales. Any scales of adequate capacity and accuracy can be used. While weighing, the machine should be relatively level to reduce error caused by weight transfer. Enough loads should be weighed to provide a good average. Machine weight is the sum of the individual wheel or axle weights.

*Drawbar Pounds Pull
**Source: Caterpillar Tractor Company

The weight of the load can be determined using the empty and loaded weight of the unit.

$$\text{Weight of load} = \text{Gross vehicle weight} - \text{empty weight}$$

To determine the bank cubic measure (BCY = bank cubic yards; BCM = bank cubic meters) carried by a machine, the load weight is divided by the bank-state density of the material being hauled.

$$BCY = \frac{\text{weight of load}}{\text{bank density}}$$

Time Studies

To estimate production, the number of complete trips a unit makes per hour must be determined. First, however, the unit's cycle time must be obtained. This is easily calculated with the help of a stop watch. Several complete cycles must be timed to arrive at an average cycle time. By allowing the watch to run continuously, different segments such as load time, wait time, etc., can be recorded for each cycle. Knowing the individual time segments affords a good opportunity to evaluate the balance of the spread and job efficiency. The following is an example of a scraper load time study form:

TOTAL CYCLE TIMES (LESS DELAYS)	ARRIVE CUT	WAIT TIME	BEGIN LOAD	LOAD TIME	END LOAD	BEGIN DELAY	DELAY TIME	END DELAY
	0.00	0.30	0.30	0.60	0.90			
3.50	3.50	0.30	3.80	0.65	4.45			
4.00	7.50	0.35	7.85	0.70	8.55	9.95	1.00	10.95
4.00	12.50	0.42	12.92	0.68	13.60			

This may be easily extended to include other segments of the cycle such as haul time, dump time, etc. Similar forms can be made for pushers, loaders, dozers, etc. *Wait time* is the time a unit must wait for another unit so that the two can function together (haul unit waiting for pusher). *Delay time* is any time, other than wait time, when a machine is not performing in the work cycle (scraper waiting to cross railroad track).

To determine trips per hour at 100% efficiency, divide 60 minutes by the average cycle time less all wait and delay time. Cycle time may or may not include wait and/or delay time. Therefore, it is possible to figure different kinds of production: measured production, production without wait or delay, maximum production, etc. For example:

Actual Production: includes all wait and delay time.

Production (without delays): includes wait time that is considered normal but no delay time.

Maximum Production: to figure maximum (or optimum) production, both wait time and delay time are eliminated. The cycle time may be further altered by using an optimum load time as determined from a load growth study.

Example (English measure)

A job study of a wheel tractor–scraper might yield the following information:

Average wait time	$= 0.28$ minute
Average load time	$= 0.65$
Average delay time	$= 0.25$
Average haul time	$= 4.26$
Average dump time	$= 0.50$
Average return time	$\underline{= 2.09}$
Average total cycle	$\underline{= 8.03}$
Less wait & delay time	$= 0.53$
Average cycle 100% eff.	$= 7.50$ minutes

Weight of haul unit empty $= 48{,}650$ lb
Weights of haul unit loaded $=$
Weighing unit #1 $= 93{,}420$ lb
Weighing unit #2 $= 89{,}770$ lb
Weighing unit #3 $= \underline{88{,}760}$ lb
$271{,}950$ lb; average $= 90{,}650$ lb

Find (1) average load weight, (2) bank density, (3) load, (4) number of cycles per hour, and (5) production, less delays, of the tractor–scraper unit.

(1) Average load weight $= 90{,}650$ lb $- 48{,}650$ lb $= 42{,}000$ lb

(2) Bank density $= 3{,}125$ lb/BCY

(3) Load $= \dfrac{\text{Weight of load}}{\text{Bank density}} = \dfrac{42{,}000 \text{ lb}}{3{,}125 \text{ lb/BCY}} = 13.4$ BCY

(4) Cycles/hr $= \dfrac{60 \text{ min/hr}}{\text{cycle time}} = \dfrac{60 \text{ min/hr}}{7.50 \text{ min/cycle}} = 8.0$ cycles/hr

(5) Production $\quad= \text{Load/cycle} \times \text{cycles/hr}$
(less delays) $= 13.4$ BCY/cycle $\times 8.0$ cycles/hr
$= 107.2$ BCY/hr

*Example
(Metric
system)*

A job study of a wheel tractor–scraper might yield the following information:

$$\begin{aligned}
\text{Average wait time} &= 0.28 \text{ minute}\\
\text{Average load time} &= 0.65\\
\text{Average delay time} &= 0.25\\
\text{Average haul time} &= 4.26\\
\text{Average dump time} &= 0.50\\
\text{Average return time} &= \underline{2.09}\\
\text{Average total cycle} &= \underline{8.03}\\
\text{Less wait \& delay time} &= 0.53\\
\text{Average cycle 100\% eff.} &= 7.50 \text{ minutes}
\end{aligned}$$

Weight of haul unit empty = 22,070 kg
Weights of haul unit loaded =
  Weighing unit #1 = 42,375 kg
  Weighing unit #2 = 40,720 kg
  Weighing unit #3 = <u>40,260 kg</u>
            123,355 kg; average = 41,120 kg

Find (1) average load weight, (2) bank density, (3) load, (4) number of cycles per hour, and (5) production, less delays, of the tractor–scraper unit.

1. Average load weight = 41,120 kg − 22,070 kg = 19,050 kg

2. Bank density = 1,854 kg/BCM

3. Load = $\dfrac{\text{weight of load}}{\text{bank density}} = \dfrac{19,050 \text{ kg}}{1,854 \text{ kg/BCM}} = 10.3$ BCM

4. Cycles/hr = $\dfrac{60 \text{ min/hr}}{\text{Cycle time}} = \dfrac{60 \text{ min/hr}}{7.50 \text{ min/cycle}} = 8.0$ cycles/hr

5. Production = Load/cycle × cycles/hr
   (less delays) = 10.3 BCM/cycle × 8.0 cycles/hr
            = 82 BCM/hr

ESTIMATING DOZER PRODUCTION ON THE JOB

Three generally accepted methods of measuring bulldozer production are listed below. The third method is empirical, but is the simplest to conduct.

1. Employing Surveying Techniques

a. Conduct time study and then cross-section the cut to determine the volume of material removed. (Production in bank cubic yards (BCY) or bank cubic meters (BCM) per unit of time)

b. Conduct time study and then cross-section the fill to determine the volume of fill material. (Production in loose cubic yards (LCY) or loose cubic meters (LCM) per unit of time)

2. Weighing Blade Loads

    Conduct time study and weigh material moved by bulldozer by weighing the loader bucket loads.

3. Measuring Blade Loads

    a. Dozer operation

       (1) Pick up and carry load onto a level area and stop.

       (2) Raise the blade directly over the pile pulling forward slightly as blade comes up, leaving a nearly symmetrical pile.

       (3) Reverse to clear the pile.

    b. Measurements

       (1) The average *height (H)* of the pile in feet. Hold the tape vertically at the inside edge of each grouser mark. Sight along top of the pile to obtain the correct measurement.

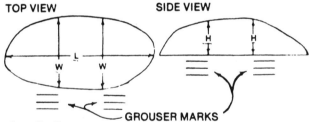

Source: Caterpillar Tractor

       (2) The average *width (W)* of the pile in feet. Hold the tape horizontally over the pile and sight at the inside edge of each grouser mark and the corresponding opposite side of the pile.

       (3) The greatest *length (L)* of the pile in feet. Hold the tape horizontally over the pile and sight at each end of the pile.

    c. With the above measurements, now compute the blade load.

       (1) Average the height measurement *(H)*

       (2) Average the width measurement *(W)*

       (3) Load (LCY or LCM) $= 0.0138 \times (HWL)$

       (4) Load (BCY or BCM) $=$ LCY or LCM $\times$ LF

    d. Combine the calculated blade load with time study to figure production.

PROBLEMS

Problem 1

Construct a 10,000-compacted-cubic-yard bridge approach of dry clay with a shrinkage factor of 0.80 and load factor of 0.81. Haul unit is rated 14 loose cubic yards struck and 20 loose cubic yards heaped.
a. How many bank yards are needed?
b. How many loads are required?

a. $BCY = \dfrac{CCY}{S.F.} = \dfrac{10,000}{0.80} = 12,500 \ BCY$

b. $Load \ (BCY) = Capacity \ (LCY) \times L.F. = 20 \times 0.81$
$$= 16.2 \ BCY/load$$

$$Number \ of \ loads \ required = \dfrac{12,500 \ BCY}{16.2 \ BCY/load} = 772 \ loads$$

Problem 2

A crawler tractor is to be used to move clay an average distance of 100 feet and return an average distance of 120 feet. The dozer will be operated in second gear forward and high gear reverse. The dozer blade is straight, and shuttle dozing will be used. Also:

1. Blade capacity is 2.6 cubic yards.
2. Efficiency factor of the dozer is .83.
3. Maximum speed in second gear forward is 2.4 mph; maximum speed in high gear reverse is 5.5 mph.
4. Soil conversion factor is .70 loose to in-place.

How many bank cubic yards of clay can be moved per hour?

Solution: First, find the variable time:

$$Variable \ time = \dfrac{haul \ distance \ (feet)}{mph \times 88} + \dfrac{return \ distance \ (feet)}{mph \times 88}$$

$$= \dfrac{100}{2.4 \times 88} + \dfrac{120}{5.5 \times 88} = .722 \ minute$$

Next, compute cycle time:

$$Cycle \ time = fixed \ time + variable \ time$$

Manufacturer's tables list fixed time as 0.2 minute; therefore,

$$\text{Cycle time} = .2 + .722 = .922 \text{ minute.}$$

Now, estimate output:

$$\text{Output} = \frac{\text{blade capacity} \times \text{soil conversion factor} \times 60 \text{ min/hr} \times \text{efficiency}}{\text{cycle time}}$$

$$= \frac{2.6 \times .70 \times 60 \times .83}{.922} = \frac{90.6}{.922} = 98.3 \text{ bank cu yd/hr}$$

Problem 3

The project is an earth fill levee. Job conditions are as follows:

1. Compacted earth fill required, 100,000 cu yd dry earth loam.
2. Initial moisture content, 10%.
3. Average haul distance, 8,400 ft.
4. Grade of haul road to fill, +4%.
5. Condition of haul road: rutted clay loam, 1 inch or more tire penetration under load.
6. Elevation is 3,000 ft.
7. Workdays to be 10 hrs.
8. Equipment: 10 tractors with scrapers, scrapers with capacity of 18 cu yd.

Solution: Rolling resistance *(RR)* = gross weight of rolling unit in tons × rolling resistance per ton. Manufacturer's specs list weight of tractor at 52,000 lb, scraper, 38,900 lb. Total weight of empty rig is 52,000 lb + 38,900 lb = 91,100 lb.

Weight of load:

$$\text{Scraper capacity} = 18.25 \text{ cu yd.}$$

$$\text{Weight of loose, dry soil} = 1,950 \text{ lb/cu yd.}$$

$$\text{Weight of soil with 10\% moisture} = 1,950 \times 1.10 = 2,145 \text{ lb/cu yd.}$$

$$\text{Weight of load} = 2,145 \times 18.25 = 38,950 \text{ lb/load.}$$

Rolling resistance factor for rutted clay loam with 1-inch penetration $=$ 100 lb/ton.

$$RR \text{ for empty rig} = \frac{91,100 \text{ lb}}{2,000 \text{ lb/ton}} \times 100 = 4,555 \text{ DBPP*}.$$

$$RR \text{ for loaded rig} = \frac{91,100 \text{ lb} + 38,950 \text{ lb}}{2,000 \text{ lb/ton}} \times 100 = 6,500 \text{ DBPP}$$

Grade resistance $(GR) =$ gross weight of rig in tons $\times$ 20 lb/ton $\times$ percent slope.

$$GR \text{ to fill} = \frac{91,100 \text{ lb} + 38,950 \text{ lb}}{2,000 \text{ lb/ton}} \times 20 \times 4 = 5,200 \text{ DBPP}$$

$$GR, \text{ return} = \frac{91,100 \text{ lb}}{2,000 \text{ lb/ton}} \times 20 \times 4 = 3,644 \text{ DBPP}$$

Traction limitation $=$ weight on drive wheels $\times$ coefficient of traction.

Manufacturer's specs give weight on drive wheels as 74%. Thus, available DBPP $= 52,200$ lb $\times .74 = 36,628$ lb. Coefficient of traction for rubber tires on rutted clay loam is 0.40. Thus, usable DBPP $= 36,628 \times 0.40 = 15,451$ lb.

Total pull required $= RR$ (loaded) $+ GR = 11,700$ DBPP required, which is less than 15,451 usable; therefore, the tractor can pull the load.

$$\text{Haul time to fill} = \frac{\text{haul distance}}{\text{speed in mph} \times 88}$$

DBPP required $= 11,700$

From the manufacturer's rimpull vs. speed chart for the particular rubber-tired tractor, using a rimpull of 11,700 pounds and reading for second gear, the speed is found to be approximately 7.5 mph.

$$\text{Time required} = \frac{88,400 \text{ ft}}{7.5 \text{ mph} \times 88} = 12.8 \text{ minutes}$$

Return travel time:

Return trip is downhill; therefore, GR (return) becomes grade assistance (GA) and must be subtracted from total pull required. Thus,

DBPP required $= RR$ empty $- GA = 4,555 - 3,644 = 911$ DBPP required

---

*Drawbar Pounds Pull

From the manufacturer's rimpull vs. speed chart, using a rimpull of 911 pounds and reading for third gear, the speed is approximately 30 mph. Thus,

$$\text{Return travel time} = \frac{30 \text{ mph} \times 88}{8,400 \text{ ft}} = 3.2 \text{ minutes}$$

Total cycle time = haul time + return time + fixed time. Fixed time, from the manufacturer's charts, is 2.0 minutes. Third-gear time is used as an average for estimating purposes. Accordingly,

$$\text{Cycle time} = 12.8 + 3.2 + 2.0 = 18.0 \text{ minutes}$$

Production per day = number of loads per hour × volume of load × number of units × number of hours per day × efficiency factor (efficiency factor is .75). So

$$\text{Production per day} = \frac{60 \text{ min/hr}}{18 \text{ min/cycle}} \times 18.25 \text{ cu yd} \times 10 \text{ units} \times 10 \text{ hr/day} \times .75$$

$$= 4,562 \text{ loose cubic yards}$$

Conversion factors: in-place to loose = 1.25; in-place to compacted = .90. Thus,

$$\frac{4,562 \text{ cu yd}}{1.25} \times .90 = 3,284 \text{ cu yd compacted per day}$$

Time to complete project:

$$\frac{100,000 \text{ cu yd required}}{3,284 \text{ cu yd per day}} = 30.4 \approx 31 \text{ days}$$

Problem 4*

Determine the average hourly production of a Caterpillar D8/8S (with tilt cylinder) moving hard-packed clay an average distance of 150 feet (45 meters) down a 15% grade, using a slot dozing technique.

Estimated material weight is 2,650 lb/LCY (1,600 kg/LCM). Operator is average. Job efficiency is estimated at 50 min/hr.

Uncorrected Maximum Production—785 LCY/hr (600 LCM/hr) (example only)

*Source: Caterpillar Tractor Company

Applicable Correction Factors:

Hard-packed clay is "hard to cut" material .... −0.80
Grade correction (from graph) .... −1.19
Slot dozing .... −1.20
Average operator .... −0.75
Job efficiency (50 min/hr) .... −0.84
Weight correction .... (2300/2650) −0.87

(See Figure 12–10.)

Solution: Production = maximum production × correction factors

= (785 LCY/hr) (0.80) (1.19) (1.20) (0.75) (0.84) (0.87)

= 491 LCY/hr

To obtain production in metric units, the same procedure is used, substituting maximum uncorrected production in LCM.

= 600 LCM/hr × Factors

= 375 LCM/hr

Problem 5*

A contractor is planning to put the following spread on a dam job. What is the estimated production and cost/BCY?
Equipment:

11—631D Wheet Tractor-Scrapers
2—D9L Tractors with C-dozers
2—12G Motor Graders
1—825C Tamping Foot Compactor

Material:

Description—Sandy clay; damp, natural bed
Bank Density—3000 lb/BCY
Load Factor—0.80
Shrinkage Factor—0.85
Traction Factor—0.50
Altitude—7500 ft.

*Source: Caterpillar Tractor Company

JOB CONDITION CORRECTION FACTORS

	TRACK-TYPE TRACTOR	WHEEL-TYPE TRACTOR
OPERATOR —		
Excellent	1.00	1.00
Average	0.75	0.60
Poor	0.60	0.50
MATERIAL —		
Loose stockpile	1.20	1.20
Hard to cut; frozen —		
with tilt cylinder	0.80	0.75
without tilt cylinder	0.70	—
cable controlled blade	0.60	—
Hard to drift; "dead" (dry, non-cohesive material) or very sticky material	0.80	0.80
Rock, ripped or blasted	0.60-0.80	—
SLOT DOZING	1.20	1.20
SIDE BY SIDE DOZING	1.15-1.25	1.15-1.25
VISIBILITY —		
Dust, rain, snow, fog or darkness	0.80	0.70
JOB EFFICIENCY —		
50 min/hr	0.84	0.84
40 min/hr	0.67	0.67
DIRECT DRIVE TRANSMISSION		
(0.1 min. fixed time)	0.80	—
BULLDOZER*		
Angling (A) blade	0.50-0.75	—
Cushioned (C) blade	0.50-0.75	0.50-0.75
D5 narrow gauge	0.90	—
Light material U-blade (coal)	1.20	1.20
GRADES — See following graph.		

*Note: Angling blades and cushion blades are not considered production dozing tools. Depending on job conditions, the A-blade and C-blade will average 50-75% of straight blade production.

(a)

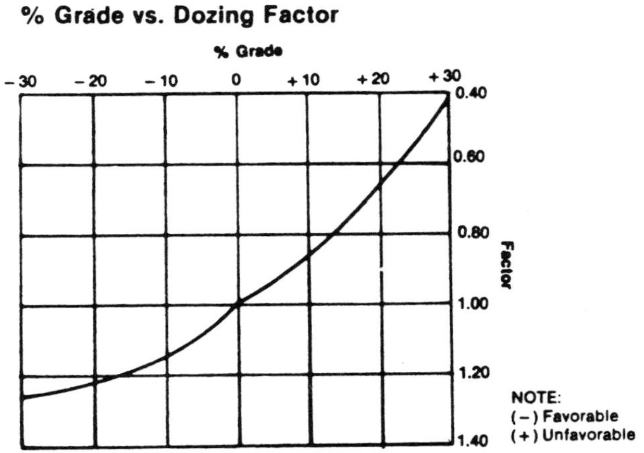

% Grade vs. Dozing Factor

Source: Caterpillar Tractor

(b)

Figure 12–10. (a) Job condition correction factors. (b) Grade correction.

227

Job Layout—Haul and Return:

Total Effective Grade = *RR* (%) ± *GR* (%)

Sec. A: Total Effective Grade = 10% + 0% = 10%
Sec. B: Total Effective Grade = 4% + 0% = 4%
Sec. C: Total Effective Grade = 4% + 4% = 8%
Sec. D: Total Effective Grade = 10% + 0% = 10%

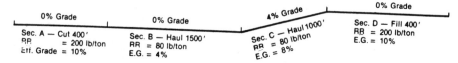

Solution:

1. Estimate Payload:

$$\text{Est. load (LCY)} \times \text{L.F.} \times \text{bank density} = \text{payload}$$

$$31 \text{ LCY} \times 0.80 \times 3{,}000 \text{ lb/BCY} = 74{,}400 \text{ lb payload}$$

2. Establish Machine Weight:

Empty Wt. — 88,000 lb or 44 tons
Wt. of Load — 74,400 lb or 37.2 tons
Total (GVW)—162,400 lb or 81.2 tons

3. Calculate Usable Pull (traction limitation):

Loaded: (weight on driving wheels = 54%) (GVW)

$$\text{Traction Factor} \times \text{Wt. on driving wheels} =$$

$$0.50 \times 162{,}400 \text{ lb} \times 54\% = 43{,}848 \text{ lb}$$

Empty: (weight on driving wheels = 69%) (GVW)

$$\text{Traction Factor} \times \text{Wt. on driving wheels} =$$

$$0.50 \times 88{,}000 \text{ lb} \times 69\% = 30{,}360 \text{ lb}$$

4. Derate for Altitude:

Check power available at 7,500 ft from altitude deration table in the Tables Section.

631D—100%
D9L—100%
12G—85%
825C—94%

Then adjust if necessary:

Load Time—controlled by D9L, at 100% power, no change.
Travel, Maneuver and Spread time—631D, no change.

5. Compare Total Resistance to Tractive Effort on haul:

Grade Resistance—

$$GR = \text{lb/ton} \times \text{tons} \times \text{adverse grade in percent}$$

$$\text{Sec. C:} = 20 \text{ lb/ton} \times 81.5 \text{ tons} \times 4\% \text{ grade} = 6{,}520 \text{ lb}$$

Rolling Resistance—

$$RR = RR \text{ Factor (lb/ton)} \times \text{GVW (tons)}$$

$$\text{Sec. A:} = 200 \text{ lb/ton} \times 81.2 \text{ tons} = 16{,}240 \text{ lb.}$$

$$\text{Sec. B:} = 80 \text{ lb/ton} \times 81.2 \text{ tons} = 6{,}496 \text{ lb}$$

$$\text{Sec. C:} = 80 \text{ lb/ton} \times 81.2 \text{ tons} = 6{,}496 \text{ lb}$$

$$\text{Sec. D:} = 200 \text{ lb/ton} \times 81.2 \text{ tons} = 16{,}240 \text{ lb}$$

Total Resistance—

$$TR = RR + GR$$

$$\text{Sec. A:} = 16{,}240 \text{ lb} + 0 = 16{,}240 \text{ lb}$$

$$\text{Sec. B:} = 6{,}496 \text{ lb} + 0 = 6{,}496 \text{ lb}$$

$$\text{Sec. C:} = 6{,}496 \text{ lb} + 6{,}496 \text{ lb} = 12{,}992 \text{ lb}$$

$$\text{Sec. D:} = 16{,}240 \text{ lb} + 0 = 16{,}240 \text{ lb}$$

Check usable pounds pull against maximum pounds pull required to move the 631D.

Pull usable . . . 43,848 lb loaded

Pull required . . . 16,240 lb maximum total resistance

Estimate travel time for haul from 631D (loaded) travel time curve; read travel time from distance and effective grade (charts available from Caterpillar).

Travel time (from curves) = 3.40 min
    Sec. A: 0.60 min
    Sec. B: 1.00
    Sec. C: 1.20
    Sec. D: 0.60

NOTE: This is an estimate only; it *does not account for all the acceleration and deceleration time;* therefore it is not as accurate as the information obtained from a computer program.

6. Compare Total Resistance to Tractive Effort on return:

Grade Assistance—

$$GA = 20 \text{ lb/ton} \times \text{tons} \times \text{negative grade in percent}$$

$$\text{Sec.C:} = 20 \text{ lb/ton} \times 44 \text{ tons} \times 4\% \text{ grade} = 3{,}520 \text{ lb}$$

Rolling Resistance—

$$RR = RR \text{ Factor} \times \text{Empty Wt (tons)}$$

$$\text{Sec. D:} = 200 \text{ lb/ton} \times 44 \text{ tons} = 8{,}800 \text{ lb}$$

$$\text{Sec. C:} = 80 \text{ lb/ton} \times 44 \text{ tons} = 3{,}520 \text{ lb}$$

$$\text{Sec. B:} = 80 \text{ lb/ton} \times 44 \text{ tons} = 3{,}520 \text{ lb}$$

$$\text{Sec. A:} = 200 \text{ lb/ton} \times 44 \text{ tons} = 8{,}800 \text{ lb}$$

Total Resistance—

$$TR = RR - GA$$

$$\text{Sec. D:} = 8{,}800 \text{ lb} - \quad 0 \quad = 8{,}800 \text{ lb}$$

$$\text{Sec. C:} = 3{,}520 \text{ lb} - 3{,}520 \text{ lb} = \quad 0$$

$$\text{Sec. B:} = 3{,}520 \text{ lb} - \quad 0 \quad = 3{,}520 \text{ lb}$$

$$\text{Sec. A:} = 8{,}800 \text{ lb} - \quad 0 \quad = 8{,}800 \text{ lb}$$

Check usable pounds pull against maximum pounds pull required to move the 631D.

Pounds pull usable . . . 30,360 lb empty
Pounds pull required . . . 8,800 lb
Estimate travel time for return from 631D empty travel time curve.

$$\text{Travel time (from curves)} = 2.15 \text{ min.}$$
Sec. D: 0.40 min
Sec. C: 0.55
Sec. B: 0.80
Sec. A: 0.40

7. Estimate Cycle Time:

$$\text{Total Travel Time (Haul plus Return)} = 5.55 \text{ min}$$

$$\text{Adjusted for altitude: } 100\% \times 5.55 \text{ min} = 5.55 \text{ min}$$

$$\text{Load Time} = 0.7 \text{ min}$$

$$\text{Maneuver and Spread Time} = 0.7 \text{ min}$$

$$\text{Total Cycle Time} = 6.95 \text{ min}$$

8. Check pusher–scraper combinations:

Pusher cycle time consists of load, boost, return and maneuver time. Where actual job data is not available, the following may be used.

$$\text{Boost time} = 0.10 \text{ min}$$

$$\text{Return time} = 40\% \text{ of load time}$$

$$\text{Maneuver time} = 0.15 \text{ min}$$

$$\text{Pusher cycle time} = 140\% \text{ of load time} + 0.25 \text{ min}$$

$$\text{Pusher cycle time} = 140\% \text{ of } 0.7 \text{ min} + 0.25 \text{ min}$$

$$= 0.98 + 0.25 = 1.23 \text{ min}$$

Scraper cycle time divided by pusher cycle time indicates the number of scrapers which can be handled by each pusher.

$$\frac{6.95 \text{ min}}{1.23 \text{ min}} = 5.65$$

Each push tractor is capable of handling five-plus scrapers. Therefore the two pushers can adequately serve the eleven scrapers.

9. Estimate Production:

$$\text{Cycles/hour} = 60 \text{ min} \div \text{Total cycle time}$$

$$= 60 \text{ min/hr} \div 6.95 \text{ min/cycle}$$

$$= 8.6 \text{ cycles/hr}$$

$$\text{Estimated load} = \text{Heaped capacity} \times \text{L.F.}$$

$$= 31 \text{ LCY} \times 0.80$$

$$= 24.8 \text{ BCY}$$

$$\text{Hourly unit production} = \text{Est. load} \times \text{cycles/hr}$$

$$= 24.8 \text{ BCY} \times 8.6 \text{ cycles/hr}$$

$$= 213.28 \text{ BCY/hr}$$

$$\text{Adjusted production} = \text{Efficiency factor} \times \text{hourly production}$$

$$= 0.83 \ (50\text{-min hour}) \times 213.28 \ \text{BCY}$$

$$= 177 \ \text{BCY/hr}$$

$$\text{Hourly fleet production} = \text{Unit production} \times \text{No. of units}$$

$$= 177 \ \text{BCY/hr} \times 11$$

$$= 1{,}947 \ \text{BCY/hr}$$

10. Estimate Compaction:

$$\text{Compaction requirement} = \text{S.F.} \times \text{hourly fleet production}$$

$$= 0.85 \times 1{,}947 \ \text{BCY/hr}$$

$$= 1{,}655 \ \text{CCY/hr}$$

Compaction capability (given the following):

Compacting width, 7.4 ft	*(W)*
Average compacting speed, 6 mph	*(S)*
Compacted lift thickness, 7 in.	*(L)*
No. of passes required, 3	*(P)*

825C production =

$$\text{CCY/hr} = \frac{W \times S \times L \times 16.3}{P} \quad \text{(conversion constant)}$$

$$= \frac{7.4 \times 6 \times 7 \times 16.3}{3}$$

$$= 1{,}688.68 \ \text{CCY/hr}$$

Given the compaction requirement of 1,655 CCY/hr, the 825C is an adequate compactor match-up for the rest of the fleet. However, any change to job layout that would increase fleet production would upset this balance. A factor to watch.

11. Estimate Total Hourly Cost:

631D	@$65.00/hr × 11 units	$715.00
D9L	@ 75.00/hr × 2 units	150.00
12G	@ 15.00/hr × 2 units	30.00
825C	@ 40.00/hr × 1 unit	40.00
Operators @ 20.00/hr × 16 men		320.00
Total Hourly Owning and Operating Cost		$1,255.00

12. Calculate Performance:

$$\text{Cost per BCY} = \frac{\text{Total cost/hr}}{\text{Production/hr}}$$

$$= \frac{\$1,255.00}{1,947 \text{ BCY/hr}}$$

$$= 64\text{¢/BCY}$$

NOTE: Ton-MPH calculations should be made to judge the ability of the tractor–scraper tires to operate safely under these conditions.

13. Other Considerations:

If other equipment such as rippers, water wagons, discs or other miscellaneous machines are needed for the particular operation, then these machines must also be included in the cost per BCY.

APPENDIX

GLOSSARY*

Add-On Interest: Interest expressed in dollars per hundred per year, i.e., 10% add-on is 10 dollars per hundred per year.

Adjusted Tax Basis: The net amount used to calculate depreciation and investment tax credit.

Coefficient of Traction: The ratio of the maximum pounds pull (before the drivers slip) to the weight on the drivers.

Compaction: The increase in density from loose material to compacted material.

Crowding Force: The force that pushes the bucket into the bank. It is a function of power available, hydraulic power, and linkage design.

Cycle Time: The time for a machine to complete one cycle, i.e., load, haul, dump and return.

Density: The weight of material in a given volume.

Depreciation Factor: The percentage of the adjusted tax basis that is depreciated over the depreciation period.

Drawbar Pull: A track machine's power available measured at the draw hitch.

Dump Time: The time it takes to empty the bucket, bowl, etc.

Efficiency Factors: Percentage of theoretical production obtainable under actual conditions.

Fixed Time: Load, dump, and maneuver time that are relatively constant in a cycle.

Grade Percentage: The steepness of a grade. It is measured by dividing the change in elevation by the horizontal distance.

Grade Resistance: Gravity's force that must be overcome when going up (or down) a grade.

*Source: Caterpillar Tractor Company

Gross Vehicle Weight: The total weight of the machine and payload.

Haul Time: The time it takes to travel from the load area to the dump area.

Insurance Factor: A factor used to average insurance costs over the life of a machine.

Internal Friction: The power losses in the power train from engine flywheel to the final drives.

Investment Tax Credit Percentage: The percentage of adjusted tax basis the buyer can take as a one-time deduction from taxes owed the federal government.

Load Factor: A ratio that measures the decrease in density when a BCM/BCY of material is disturbed or removed from the bank state.

Load Time: The time it takes to load a truck, fill a bucket, etc.

Operating Costs: Costs that result when a machine is being used, e.g., fuel, repair, wear items, operator wages, etc.

Owning Costs: Costs that result from owning a machine, e.g., depreciation, interest cost, insurance. These costs accrue whether a machine works or not.

Power Available: The power a machine can exert, at the drawbar for track machines, and at the wheels for rubber-tired machines.

Power Required: The amount of power needed to overcome rolling resistance and grade resistance.

Power Usable: The amount of power that can be used. Power usable is a function of power available and the coefficient of traction.

Residual Factor: The percentage of a machine's adjusted tax basis left on the books after the machine has been depreciated.

Return Time: The time it takes to travel from the dump area to the load area.

Rimpull: A wheeled machine's power available measured at the tire.

Rolling Resistance: The sum of forces (internal friction, tire flexing, tire penetration) that prevent a machine from moving on a level surface.

Shrinkage: The percentage decrease of a material's volume when compacted.

Swell: The percentage a material expands when disturbed or removed from its bank state.

Tire Flexing: Tire squashing under load.

Tire Penetration: The depth a tire sinks into the ground.

Underfoot Conditions: The surface material the machine is working in.

Variable Times: Those times (e.g., haul, return) that vary with distance and speed.

$$Production,\ hourly = \text{Load (BCY) cycle} \times \text{cycles/hr}$$

$$= \text{Load (BCM) cycle} \times \text{cycles/hr}$$

$$Load\ Factor\ (L.F.) = \frac{100\%}{100\% + \%\ \text{swell}}$$

$$Load\ (bank\ measure) = \text{Loose cubic yards (LCY)} \times \text{L.F.}$$

$$= \text{Loose cubic meters (LCM)} \times \text{L.F.}$$

$$Shrinkage\ Factor\ (S.F.) = \frac{\text{Compacted cubic yards (or meters)}}{\text{Bank cubic yards (or meters)}}$$

$$Density = \text{Weight/Unit Volume}$$

$$Load\ (bank\ measure) = \frac{\text{Weight of load}}{\text{Bank density}}$$

$$Rolling\ Resistance\ Factor = 40\ \text{lb/ton} + (30\ \text{lb/ton/inch} \times \text{inches})$$

$$= 20\ \text{kg/ton} + (6\ \text{kg/ton/cm} \times \text{cm})$$

$$Rolling\ Resistance = RR\ \text{Factor (lb/ton)} \times \text{GVW (tons)}$$

$$= RR\ \text{Factor (kg/ton)} \times \text{GVW (tons)}$$

$$Rolling\ Resistance = 2\%\ \text{of GVW} + 1.5\%\ \text{of GVW per inch tire penetration}$$

$$= 2\%\ \text{of GVW} + 0.6\%\ \text{of GVW per cm tire penetration}$$

$$\%\ Grade = \frac{\text{vertical change in elevation (rise)}}{\text{corresponding horizontal distance (run)}}$$

$$Grade\ Resistance\ Factor = 20\ \text{lb/ton} \times \%\ \text{grade}$$

$$= 10\ \text{kg/ton} \times \%\ \text{grade}$$

$$Grade\ Resistance = GR\ \text{Factor (lb/ton)} \times \text{GVW (tons)}$$

$$= GR\ \text{Factor (kg/ton)} \times \text{GVW (tons)}$$

$$Grade\ Resistance = 1\%\ \text{of GVW} \times \%\ \text{grade}$$

$$Total\ Resistance = \text{Rolling Resistance (lb or kg)} + \text{Grade Resistance (lb or kg)}$$

$$Total\ Effective\ Grade\ (\%) = RR\ (\%) + GR\ (\%)$$

*Source: Caterpillar Tractor Company

Usable pull (traction limitation) = Coeff. of traction × weight on drivers

$$= \text{Coeff. of traction} \times (\text{Total wt} \times \% \text{ on drivers})$$

Pull required = Rolling resistance + Grade Resistance

$$= \text{Total Resistance}$$

Total Cycle Time = Fixed time + Variable time

Fixed time: See respective machine production section.

Variable time = Total haul time + Total return time

$$\textit{Travel Time} = \frac{\text{Distance (ft)}}{\text{Speed (fpm)}}$$

$$= \frac{\text{Distance (m)}}{\text{Speed (m/min)}}$$

$$\textit{Cycles per hour} = \frac{60 \text{ min/hr}}{\text{Total cycle time (min/cycle)}}$$

Adjusted production = Hourly production × Efficiency factor

$$\textit{No. of units required} = \frac{\text{Hourly production required}}{\text{Unit hourly production}}$$

$$\textit{No. of scrapers a pusher will load} = \frac{\text{Scraper cycle time}}{\text{Pusher cycle time}}$$

Pusher cycle time (min) = 1.40 load time (min) + 0.25 min

GRADES OF SLOPE, AS MEASURED IN DEGREES, PERCENT, AND RATIO*

Grade in Degrees and Percents	
DEGREES	PERCENT
1	1.8
2	3.5
3	5.2
4	7.0
5	8.8
6	10.5
7	12.3
8	14.0
9	15.8
10	17.6
11	19.4
12	21.3
13	23.1
14	24.9
15	26.8
16	28.7
17	30.6
18	32.5
19	34.4
20	36.4
21	38.4
22	40.4
23	42.4
24	44.5
25	46.6
26	48.8
27	51.0
28	53.2
29	55.4
30	57.7
31	60.0
32	62.5
33	64.9
34	67.4
35	70.0
36	72.7
37	75.4
38	78.1
39	81.0
40	83.9
41	86.9
42	90.0
43	93.3
44	96.6
45	100.0

*Source: Caterpillar Tractor Company

INDEX